THE ROYAL COLLEGE OF PAEDIATRICS
AND CHILD HEALTH AT THE MILLENNIUM

Institute of Child Health, London
1966–1975

23 Queen Square 1975–1985

5 St Andrews Place 1985–1997

50 Hallam St 1997–present

Homes of the BPA and the College

Photographs taken by Christine Young.

THE ROYAL COLLEGE OF PAEDIATRICS AND CHILD HEALTH AT THE MILLENNIUM

Edited by

Bernard Valman

© Royal College of Paediatrics and Child Health 2000
50 Hallam St, London W1N 6DE

First published in 2000

British Library Cataloguing in Publication Data

A catalogue record for this book is available from the British Library

ISBN 0–7279–1434–0

Typeset by J&L Composition Ltd, Filey, North Yorkshire
Printed and bound in Great Britain by
MPG Books, Bodmin, Cornwall

Contents

Contributors

Brocklebank JT
Consultant Paediatrician
St James's University Hospital, Leeds

Profile of Roy Meadow

Chiswick ML
Professor in Child Health and Paediatrics
University of Manchester
Editor, Archives of Disease in Childhood

Profile of Bernard Valman

Cooke RW
Professor of Paediatric Medicine
Royal Liverpool Children's Hospital
Acting President, Royal College of Paediatrics and Child Health

Foreword

Craft AW
Professor of Child Health
University of Newcastle Upon Tyne
Vice President, Royal College of Paediatrics and Child Health

Donald Court: A man of vision
Profiles of George Frederic Still and James Spence

Davies DP
Professor of Child Health
University of Wales

Medical education and training in the 1990s

Davis JA
Emeritus Professor of Paediatrics and Child Health
University of Cambridge

Donald Winnicott's contribution to paediatrics

Dodd KL
Consultant Paediatrician
Derbyshire Children's Hospital, Derby

Structure of the College

Dunn PM
Emeritus Professor of Perinatal Medicine and Child Health
University of Bristol

Newborn care in the UK since 1928

Hall DMB
Professor of Community Paediatrics
University of Sheffield
President Elect, Royal College of Paediatrics and Child Health

Donald Court: A man of vision

Hamilton PA
Consultant in Neonatal Paediatrics, St George's Hospital, London
Honorary Secretary, Royal College of Paediatrics and Child Health

College strategy

Lindsay M
Honorary Consultant in Child Psychiatry
Stoke Mandeville Hospital

Development of child psychiatry services

Lynn R
Scientific Co-ordinator, BPSU

The British Paediatric Surveillance Unit

Macfarlane A
Consultant in Public Health and Health Policy
Oxfordshire Health Authority

Developing community child health, paediatrics and child public health

Mann N
Consultant Paediatrician
Royal Berkshire Hospital, Reading
Honorary Editor, Royal College of Paediatrics and Child Health

A tribute to David Baum 1940–1999

Marcovitch H
Consultant Paediatrician
Horton General Hospital Banbury
Editor, Archives of Disease in Childhood

Profile of David Baum

Meadow SR
Emeritus Professor of Paediatrics and Child Health
University of Leeds
Past President British Paediatric Association and First President Royal
College of Paediatrics and Child Health

Winning the battle for a College

Ross EM
Professor of Community Paediatrics
University of London

The British Paediatric Surveillance Unit

Spitz L
Nuffield Professor of Paediatric Surgery
Institute of Child Health and Great Ormond Street Hospital

Development of surgery and anaesthesia

Stephenson TJ
Professor of Child Health
University of Nottingham

Profile of David Hall

Stevens DW
Consultant Paediatrician and Senior Lecturer
Gloucestershire Royal Hospital

Profile of Helen Mackay

Sumner E
Consultant Anaesthetist
Great Ormond Street Hospital

Development of surgery and anaesthesia

Valman HB
Consultant Paediatrician, Northwick Park Hospital and Honorary
Archivist, Royal College of Paediatrics and Child Health

Editor and Preface
The British Paediatric Association and the College
Profile of Malcolm Chiswick
Archives of Disease in Childhood

West R
Consultant Paediatrician and Regional Postgraduate Dean
University of Bristol

Profile of June Lloyd

Foreword

For children born in the 20th century, the chances of surviving childhood were never better, at least in the more economically privileged nations. The dramatic fall in childhood mortality and morbidity were intially due to a rapid improvement in socio-economic circumstances, and legislation to improve living conditions. Later medical factors such as the introduction of immunisation, improved maternal and neonatal care, and the introduction of advanced paediatric surgery contributed to further improvements. After the Second World War, the development of a National Health Service contributed particularly to the improved health and welfare of children.

The science and art of paediatrics and child health developed more slowly in the UK compared with many other European countries or North America. Whilst physicians and surgeons for adults both had Royal Colleges to support their members and ensure standards in their craft, paediatricians had felt marginalised. The formation of a College of Paediatrics and Child Health was a long haul, and took several decades to achieve. The successful establishment of the College in 1996 was an important step for the progress of children's medicine in this country, and has brought community and hospital based paediatricians together under one roof. Training and standard setting in the profession are also now in the hands of those most concerned with the health of children.

Other major developments that have occurred include the growing understanding amongst paediatricians and others of the importance of the early nurturing of children for their mental and developmental health. Despite the improvements that have occurred in the welfare of children, huge inequalities still exist. Physical violence towards children has decreased with better understanding, but neglect and other abuses are still common, and their management makes up a large part of day to day paediatric practice.

Finally, as the world becomes a smaller place, with the development of widespread access to international communications, we as a college for children are aware of the plight and health needs of children everywhere. This last century has been unprecedented in its violence and warfare. Children are some of the first victims of such conflicts. While our efforts can at best only make a small contribution, they are still justified. Our College has much to tackle in the years ahead.

Richard Cooke
Acting President, Royal College
of Paediatrics and Child Health

Preface

In 1994 David Baum wrote asking whether he could interest me in a new slice of work to fill the leisure time I would face on stepping down from my post as Editor of *Archives of Disease in Childhood.* The Executive Committee of the British Paediatric Association (BPA) had suggested that he should approach me. The new post was Contemporary Historian (or Archivist) and the objective was to collect material prospectively for a volume covering the period 1988 to the year 2000. I accepted the post, but enthusiasm by the Executive Committee was overshadowed by the enormous continuous effort needed to sustain the fight for a College (see page 78) and the uncertainty as to whether and when a College would be founded. There was little support for a volume covering only the 12 years to the millennium and with the support of Roy Meadow, the President, and David Baum, I widened the scope of the volume. The founding of the Royal College of Paediatrics and Child Health as the successor to the BPA in 1996, provided the confirmation that a celebratory book was needed.

As in so many other areas, David's prediction that the events of the closing years of the last century would be of great historical significance for the medical care of children, their parents and paediatricians was correct. Sadly, he died while taking part in a College event and all who knew and worked with him were devastated. He knew how to distinguish the important from the trivial and led the College in its infancy with courage, inventiveness and tact.

This volume, published to mark the millennium, highlights the early years of the Royal College of Paediatrics and Child Health and gives glimpses of its predecessor, the British Paediatric Association. I have drawn heavily on previous work by historians of the BPA in the following publications:

The British Paediatric Association 1928–1952 by H C Cameron
The British Paediatric Association 1952–1968 by V Neale
The British Paediatric Association 1928–1988 by J O Forfar, A D M Jackson and B M Laurance.

The next volume in that series is due to be published in 2008. As well as original articles the present volume reviews evidence that the development of medical services for children depended on the determination of a few individual paediatricians.

I wish to thank Professor Richard Cooke for writing the Foreword and all the authors of the papers. This project was financed jointly by the Royal College of Paediatrics and Child Health and the Journals Publication Committee of the British Medical Association.

Bernard Valman
Honorary Archivist
Royal College of Paediatrics and Child Health

A tribute to David Baum 1940–1999

John David Baum, president of our College, died in office, suddenly and unexpectedly on 5th September 1999 during the Palace to Palace charity cycle ride. From its inception David had decided to be an active participant in this major fund raising venture both for the College and also for children of war-torn areas.

David was 59 years old, qualified in Birmingham 34 years ago and had been Professor of Child Health at the University of Bristol for the past 14 years; before this he had been Lecturer and subsequently Reader in Child Health in Oxford. He was born into a close Jewish family during the blitz, and was the fourth of five children of Polish immigrant parents, all of whom took up careers in either medicine or biological sciences.

David always stressed the importance of a **child-centred health service**, acting in the best interests of the child and respecting the views and wishes of children, wherever possible, in their treatment. Being a dynamic and charismatic figure, albeit of short stature, he won the respect of both colleagues and patients, not only for his undoubted learning and skill as a clinician, but for his kindness, modesty, humanity and approachability. He was always courteous and never too busy to talk to or to listen to others.

David loved children and was an expert in creating ways of entertaining youngsters in his care. By virtue of extravagant bow ties, mop of curly hair and natural eccentricity, he was affectionately known by some of his patients as "Dr Who".

In April 1997 having been elected President by our membership, he commenced his term of office. Previously he had served as Chairman of the Academic Board 1984–87 and as its Secretary for 3 years prior to this. At the age of 35 David had been awarded the BPA's Guthrie Medal in York for outstanding medical research. He was a founding member of the BPSU Executive Committee, set up in 1986, and was subsequently its Chairman until 1990. Prior to his presidency of the College, David was Director of the Research Unit.

David Baum was a distinguished paediatrician with an international reputation. As a clinician he has been responsible for two major innovations. First, he was one of the early pioneers of the human milk pasteuriser, which made it possible to set up human milk banks. Although temporarily out of fashion, milk banks are once again being seen as important for neonatal care. He was also the inventor of the "silver swaddler" – a cheap but very efficient device for preventing hypothermia in early born infants.

He conducted groundbreaking research in the care of the newborn, infant nutrition, diabetes mellitus and in hospice and respite care for children. His book, *Care of the Child with Diabetes* is a standard text. He was a member of the Joint Working Party that produced the *Guide to the Development of Children's Palliative Care Services*. In the field of palliative care he has also published the seminal work: *Listen, my child has a lot of living to do – the care of children with life threatening diseases and their families*. Helen House, the first children's hospice in Britain, was established due to David Baum's support for the venture.

At the University of Bristol David was the founding Director of the Institute of Child Health in 1988 and developed it into one of the leading institutions in its field.

As our President he oversaw a critical stage in the development and expansion of the College. His tact and diplomacy ensured that the difficult and sometimes acrimonious birth of the College neither divided paediatricians nor damaged relations with others, who doubted the wisdom of the move. During his term of office the College took over statutory responsibilities for the training of paediatricians, started to run its own examinations and expanded its membership from 4000 to more than 5000 members. He pushed for and was successful in allowing an external lay observer on our College Council.

Simultaneously to these measures he has ensured that the College became more outward looking – this was no doubt helped by his international paediatric perspective. Two personal initiatives as President were a project to improve the standard of paediatric services in Gaza, and the setting up (with the support of the Princess Royal) of an International Task Force to send paediatricians to help children in areas of conflict and natural disaster. This latter project coincided with the emergency in the Balkans and allowed the College to work alongside other agencies delivering aid to refugee children. He was also, *ad personam*, a member of the Executive Board of UNICEF (UK).

His eminence in paediatrics was recognised by invitations to serve on a number of other national bodies including the NICE Partners Council, the Councils of the King's Fund and GMC, and the Specialist Training Authority. He was elected one of the founding fellows of the new Academy of Medical Sciences.

Outside medicine David's interests were protean. He was a connoisseur of the visual arts, an interest he shared with Angela his wife; he was on the academic board of the Music Therapy Diploma in Bristol, as well as being a stimulating conversationalist and party lover. David was a prominent member of the local Jewish community in Bristol. Ultimately David was a family man and was always keen to escape London to his home. Angela, who he married in 1967 and his four sons Buzz, Josh, Jake and Sam survive him.

Nick Mann

Chapter 1: The British Paediatric Association (BPA) and the College

Bernard Valman

The following pages give a decade by decade history of the British Paediatric Association and the College.

The Early Years 1928–1938

Shortly after the First World War Donald Paterson, an eloquent and forceful Canadian paediatrician who had qualified in Edinburgh came to London. He had visited the new schools of paediatrics which had recently been founded in the USA and had become the leading international centres after the decline of Germany. He was impressed by the achievements of the American Paediatric Society both in the political arena and the scientific presentations at the Annual General Meeting and he was determined to found a Paediatric Association for all Britain. About this time every medical school in the British Isles was establishing a special department for the management of diseases of children and high quality recruits returning from the war became paediatricians with no responsibilities for adult patients for the first time.

Donald Paterson

Predecessors

The Society for the Study of Children's Diseases was the earliest predecessor of the BPA and was founded in London in 1900 with more than 800 members drawn from all parts of Britain but it disappeared within a few years. Also in London at this time was the Children's Clinical Club, a select group of a dozen consultants who met in each others homes. John Thomson of Edinburgh was the leading force and the club closed in 1926, shortly after his death. Hector Cameron and David Forsyth started a dining club to foster cooperation between those people who provided pre- and postnatal care (the Pre posterous Club). Members included obstetricians, medical officers of health and paediatricians and it fostered interest in common problems. The Edinburgh and Glasgow paediatric club was formed in 1922 and had meetings twice a year. The Provincial Children's Club started in 1924 and meetings were held in hotels in the main cities.

Inauguration

The inaugural meeting of the BPA was held at George Frederic Still's house at 26 Queen Anne's Street (near Harley Street, London) on 2nd February 1928.

Twenty four invitations were sent out but only six attended. Still was asked to take the chair as he had long been accepted as leader of those interested in the diseases of children and one of the few that practised only paediatrics. He owed his reputation to his vast clinical experience but was slow to be convinced of the need for change. Donald Paterson was elected as the first Secretary and the Executive Committee had members from London, the provinces, Scotland and Ireland. Paterson insisted that the Annual General Meeting should be held in the country and the first was held at the Old England Hotel in Windermere with 45 members. The pattern of meetings did not change for the next 20 years. There were two mornings of scientific communication, an annual dinner, golf competition, a discussion and from 1931 the showing of a film of the participants taken by Dr Wilkinson the previous year or a film of patients he had seen.

The first aim of the association was the advancement of the study of paediatrics and the promotion of friendship among paediatricians. The association had little influence on political decisions and gave most of its attention to improving the quality of the papers presented at the Annual General Meeting.

1928–1938

1922
Isolation of insulin by Banting and Best

1926
General strike

1928
Paper on high prevalence of iron deficiency anaemia published by Helen Mackay
Death of Thomas Hardy

1929
First paper by Fleming on penicillin
Crash on American Stock Exchange

1932
Renin rediscovered
The *Psychoanalysis of Children* published by Melanie Klein

1933
First description of Kwashiorkor by Cecily Williams
Hitler rises to power

1934
Reduction in unemployment due to rearmament

1935
Prontosil, first sulphonamide, introduced
Mepacrine, first synthetic antimalarial drug
The Ego and the Mechanisms of Defence published by Anna Freud

1936
Abdication of King Edward VIII

1938
Chamberlain met Hitler at Munich
Sigmund Freud and his family including his daughter Anna escaped from Vienna to London

Evacuation and the War 1938–1948

Donald Paterson and Alan Moncrieff were involved with the government in safeguarding the health of child evacuees before and during the war. Paterson drew up a memorandum and was part of a deputation to the Minister of Health to appoint paediatric consultants to coordinate measures to safeguard the health of evacuated children but this was rejected.

Meetings of the Executive Committee were held regularly in London at the home of Donald Paterson and the members' long tedious railway journeys were often interrupted by air raids. They arrived at Paterson's hospitable fireside worn and exhausted by the ordeal. Minutes of an Executive Committee meeting held in 1942 provide a flavour of the times. The committee considered reports on neonatal mortality, juvenile delinquency, immunisation, rickets, milk, vitamin D and replies to letters from the Association deploring the lack of prominence given to paediatrics in the final undergraduate examination and the proposed abolition of the sick children's nursing register. Other subjects discussed included postwar medical assistance for children (Save the Children's Fund) and a reply to the inter-departmental committee on medical schools. James Spence presented his memorandum for the Nuffield Trust in which he pointed out that there was an inadequate number of trained paediatricians because earnings in paediatric consulting practice were extremely small. Children were often scattered in adult wards and even in children's hospitals there were inadequately trained nurses and doctors. There was only one Chair of Paediatrics in England and none in London. Universities were contributing paltry amounts to teaching and he suggested that paediatric departments should foster close contact with other branches of medicine, pathology, anatomy, physiology and social sciences.

The blitz

Despite the turmoil produced by the war Leonard Parsons of Birmingham, James Spence of Newcastle and Charles McNeil of Edinburgh found full opportunity to exercise their powers of organisation, constructive criticism and vision. All three held newly established Chairs in Child Health and were constantly occupied on governmental committees. Leonard Parsons was the most prolific contributor to the knowledge of disease of his generation. Spence insisted that all new Chairs be given the title of Chairs of Child Health. McNeil was a quiet visionary whose ideas on developmental paediatrics, community care and neonatal care were ahead of his time.

Annual General Meetings continued apart from 1940 when there was a sustained air attack on Britain. In 1943 there was the first of many discussions on the proposed College of Child Health.

In 1943 and 1944 there were endless discussions, especially with the RCP and the BMA on the future of the medical profession in the proposed National Health Service.

The BPA voted to admit women members. The BPA's advice was increasingly sought when consultants were appointed.

Many prewar members of the BPA and a much larger number of more recent graduates who were to become paediatricians, served with distinction in the armed forces. Cecily Williams and Patrick McArthur were among many who suffered great privation as prisoners of war and performed outstanding work in the medical care of their fellow prisoners.

In 1947 the AGM returned to Windermere with Donald Paterson as President. The following year he returned to Canada as the idea of a National Health Service did not appeal to him.

1938–1948

1938
Austria seized by Germany

1939
Second World War begins
Evacuation of children from major cities in Britain

1940
Battle of Britain and blitz on cities
Attack on Pearl Harbour and America enters World War
D.D.T. introduced

1942
First successful clinical use of penicillin
Beveridge report on universal health insurance, social security and pensions

1944
V1 and V2 guided missiles launched on Britain
Invasion of France by Allied Forces
Butler Education Act

1945
First atomic bomb hits Hiroshima
End of Second World War
Distribution of Industry Act for reversing decline of 'depressed areas'
Labour government elected

1946
Nitrogen mustard introduced for treatment of malignancies
Noradrenaline identified as the adrenergic neurotransmitter

1948
Chloramphenicol, tetracycline and cortisone introduced

Birth of the NHS 1948–1958

The National Health Service came into operation on 5th July 1948 and rapidly improved the service to children by the appointment of many consultant paediatricians. Immediately after the war young paediatricians, whatever their abilities, could not earn sufficient if they confined themselves to paediatric practice. There were a few in London and less in the provinces. In 1948 for the first time consultants and their assistants on the staff of hospitals were remunerated. It was then possible to provide a service based on consultant paediatricians in every region of the country. The BPA urged unsuccessfully that community child health staff should be associated with the hospital service.

In 1945 the legislation that followed the recommendations of the Goodenough Report placed every medical school in the country under the control of a university. The financial resources of the universities were greatly increased and this enabled the medical schools to carry out changes in their staff and buildings. For the first time it became possible to make a payment to clinical professors, teachers, registrars and assistants at a reasonable level.

Obstetricians began to invite the paediatricians into the labour room and care of the newborn became increasingly part of the responsibility of the paediatricians. In 1953 the Executive Committee of the BPA opposed the proposal of the Ministry of Health to reduce the number of registrars. The Executive Committee bombarded the Committee with arguments that are familiar today. Children were surviving and needing medical care where they previously died. New diseases had been discovered and the advances in care needed the appointment of more consultants. The new diseases included renal

Donald Winnicott

acidosis, toxoplasmosis, cystic fibrosis, retrolental fibroplasia and subdural haematoma.

In 1956 the BPA had 200 members and it was decided that the majority of hospital paediatricians and some others with a paediatric interest should be elected to the BPA gradually over five years while maintaining the Association as a unified body undivided into specialist sections.

In 1949 Mildred Creak was the first `pure' child psychiatrist appointed a member of the BPA. Donald Winnicott had been elected in 1930 because he was on the staff of Paddington Green Children's Hospital and in charge of children with physical diseases, not because of his special interest in psychiatry.

In 1953 the Central Health Services Committee on the reception and welfare of patients in hospital encouraged frequent visiting of children in hospital.

In 1956 the Cranbrook Committee on the organisation of maternity services in England and Wales proposed that there should be greater application of recent advances in fetal and neonatal pathology and physiology and that there should be greater availability of paediatricians and obstetricians.

1948–1958

1948
National Health Service launched
Brock and Sellars heart surgery
Streptomycin introduced

1949
Power to charge for prescriptions

1950
Cortisone treatment for adrenogenital syndrome
Effect of rubella on optic lens and cardiovascular system described
Ceiling imposed on NHS spending
Korean War begins

1951
Trivalent vaccine (diphtheria, tetanus, pertussis) first recommended
Apartheid introduced in South Africa

1952
Aldosterone identified
First report on agammaglobulinaemia
Retrolental fibroplasia and possible link to oxygen treatment reported
College of General Practitioners formed
King George VI dies, Elizabeth proclaimed Queen

1953
Gibbon invents heart-lung machine
Watson and Crick propose DNA theory
Apgar describes the scoring system

1954
First kidney transplant performed

1955
Ultrasound introduced in obstetrics

1956
Polio immunisation introduced

1957
BMA report says smoking is chief cause of cancer

Education and Training 1958–1968

In the mid 1960s Douglas Hubble wrote a memorandum on specialist training for paediatricians and Gerald Neligan and Brian Webb surveyed the work of consultant paediatricians in the Newcastle, Birmingham and South West Regions.

In the spring of 1966 Tony Jackson visited all 26 undergraduate medical schools and the Departments of Clinical Paediatrics in the UK, to find details of staffing, hospital facilities and teaching programmes. A disturbing deficiency in the allocation of resources for paediatrics was revealed. These surveys formed the basis for a symposium entitled 'The Role and Training of Paediatricians in Britain' held at the Middlesex Hospital Medical School in 1968. The Academic Board formed from the previous Education Committee in 1966 with Donald Court as the new Chairman proposed the preparation of a BPA review which would act as a blueprint for paediatrics over the next decade. The review was facilitated by Ronnie MacKeith, Director of the Medical Education Information Unit of the Spastic Society which promoted informal weekend meetings of the Academic Board. The first annual scientific meeting organised by the new Academic Board in 1967 was arranged by the Board's secretary, John Davis, who grouped the papers according to subject – a concept which later developed into the specialty group meeting.

In 1966 a Minister of Health accepted the recommendations of the Platt report (1959) on the 'Welfare of Children in Hospital' that unrestricted visiting and admission of mothers with children should be implemented. Help in implementing these changes came from the National Association for the Welfare of Children in

Ronald MacKeith

Hospital (NAWCH) which had been founded in 1961. Despite central direction there was local opposition and even in 1987 a survey entitled *Where are the Children?* showed that a quarter of the children in hospital were still being cared for in wards for adults.

The annual meeting moved to the Royal Hotel at Scarborough in 1959 because the numbers attending the meetings had outgrown the luxurious Old England Hotel in Windermere. Meetings were held in Cambridge in 1961 and in Dublin in 1968 but remained at Scarborough until 1971.

In 1966 the BPA was given a small office free in the newly built Institute of Child Health in London. In 1975 Bernard Laurance negotiated the move to a larger room rented at 23 Queen's Square. This was near the Institute of Child Health which continued to provide space and office facilities.

1958–1968

1958
Identification of respiratory syncytial virus as cause of bronchiolitis
Last National Service call-up

1961
Yuri Gagarin is the first man in space
Contraceptive pill available on NHS

1962
Oral polio vaccine introduced
Kempe's paper on Child Abuse and Neglect
Hyaline membrane disease and surface active agent association
Cuban missile crisis

1963
Screening test for phenylketonuria (Guthrie) published
Homocystinuria: new inborn error of metabolism
Kennedy assassinated in Dallas
First liver transplant

1964
First clinic opens for contraceptive advice to the unmarried

1966
Measles vaccination starts
Prevention of erythroblastosis fetalis by postpartum anti-Rh immunoglobulin
Chromosome analysis of amniotic fluid cells
First comprehensive British growth charts (Tanner)

1967
First heart transplant
Abortion bill becomes law
Methylmalonic aciduria described

1968
Epidural anaesthetics promise less painful births
Martin Luther King shot dead

Paediatrics in The 1970s and the Court Report 1968–1978

In 1972 the blueprint for the next decade entitled *Paediatrics in the '70s*, edited by Court as Chairman and Jackson as Honorary Secretary of the Academic Board was published by the Oxford University Press. It led to the setting up of a Royal Commission with Donald Court as Chairman and the findings were published three years later (1976) in two volumes and became popularly known as the Court Report. The main recommendations were

- Prevention and treatment should be integrated at every level in the Child Health Service.
- General Practitioners with a special interest in training in paediatrics should be designated as `General Practitioner Paediatricians'.
- There should be designated Child Health Visitors.
- Consultant Community Paediatricians with a special interest in developmental, social and educational paediatrics should be appointed.
- Clinical Medical Officers should be absorbed into general practice or become Consultant Community Paediatricians. Senior Clinical Medical Officers should be promoted to consultant status or be replaced by consultants on retiring.
- Each district should have a district handicap team.
- The number of consultant paediatricians should be increased to provide a consultant colleague for a singlehanded paediatrician and to provide at least one community paediatrician in each district.

Although the BPA welcomed the idea of an integrated Child Health Service, the concept of General Practitioners with a special interest in Paediatrics and Health Visitors with special responsibilities for children were abandoned.

The local authority child health services were incorporated into the National Health Service in 1974 which was two years before the Court Report was published. The Senior Clinical Medical Officers and Clinical Medical Officers who were employed by the local authorities until 1974 were opposed to the Court Report and wished to maintain a separate branch of the Child Health Service working in the community separately from the general practitioner and hospital services. Discussions continued from 1976 until 1987 and involved many committees until the Alwyn Smith Committee in 1987 endorsed the views of the BPA that preventive and curative services should be combined and the third `force' integrated into the rest of the service.

In 1974 the Annual Meeting was held in Harrogate. The Academic Board invited three specialty groups to hold concurrent half-day sessions. Roy

Meadow, secretary of the Academic Board and John Davies, the Chairman, persuaded the Board to encourage the specialty groups to operate within the BPA and despite previous and continuing opposition the specialty groups were established. The following year the meeting was held in York and would remain there until 1989.

1968–1978

1969
Steptoe and Edwards pioneer test-tube fertilisation
North Sea oil discovered
Neil Armstrong is first man on moon

1970
Plans to decentralise the NHS under 90 new health authorities
Treatment of hyaline membrane disease with continuous positive pressure
Decimal currency launched
First heart and lung transplant

1971
Antepartum glucocorticoid treatment for prevention of respiratory distress syndrome

1973
First trials of haemophilus influenzae vaccine
Criteria for identifying children at risk of sudden infant death
Changes in ventilator management reduce mortality from hyaline membrane disease
Watergate hearings begin
First CAT scans
Whiplash shaken infant syndrome described by Caffey (subdural haematoma)

1974
Free family planning for all on NHS

1975
Vietnam war ends

1976
Mao Tse-Tung dies at 82

1977
Space shuttle makes maiden flight

1978
The world's first test-tube baby is born

The Tide Changes 1978–1988

In 1943 Donald Paterson had written to Mr Hempson, the Solicitor, requesting information necessary to form the BPA into a College of Child Health. The war, birth of the NHS and activities of the BPA deflected attention from a College for the next 30 years. In 1976 the Executive Committee of the BPA concluded that the BPA should become either a faculty or a college and should obtain greater authority in controlling paediatric training and achieving better representation. A year later the council of the BPA discussed a paper prepared by June Lloyd and Otto Wolff on `The Case for a College of Paediatrics'. In 1978 members were asked to vote on the question `Do you wish the association to proceed towards the promotion of a College of Paediatrics?' which resulted in 141 voting yes and 483 voting no.

Otto Wolff

In advance of the referendum the Presidents of the three Royal Colleges of Physicians issued a joint statement that they had `agreed to advise that a joint paediatric committee of the three colleges should be set up in readiness for a further discussion of a Faculty of Paediatrics within the three colleges'. The joint paediatric committee was convened and the BPA was offered full membership of the committee. The remit of the committee was to analyse and state the problems concerned with child health and to recommend to the parent bodies solutions or lines of action to be followed. This remit omitted the specific reference to a Faculty of Paediatrics made in the earlier statement but there was specific representation for paediatrics on many national committees. Encouraged by these early successes the council of the BPA imposed a moratorium on further discussion of a faculty or college for five years.

In 1986 the officers of the association prepared a comprehensive green paper entitled *The Future of the British Paediatric Association*. This discussed the advantages and disadvantages both of a joint Faculty of Paediatrics of the three

Royal Colleges of Physicians and a separate college. Following extensive discussions among members and by officers with members of the three Royal Colleges, a second referendum was held in 1987. The voting was by single transferable vote. There were 450 votes for a faculty of the Royal Colleges, 489 votes for an independent college and 71 for the *status quo*. On exclusion of the lowest option and transfer of second preferences, the position was faculty of Royal Colleges 498, independent college 506. A sub-committee was appointed and proposed to the council the following resolution: `To implement the objectives agreed at the 1987 Annual General Meeting, the council recommends steps be taken to establish a College of Paediatricians *interdependent* with the three Royal Colleges of Physicians'. The proposal was adopted by a majority of 23 to 3 at a council meeting in March 1988 and at the Annual General Meeting two months later there was an overwhelming vote in favour of an *interdependent* college. The word *interdependent* was never defined and caused considerable contro-versy. (See chapter 'Winning the battle for a College'.)

1978–1988

1980
Association between Reye's syndrome and salicylate use
Ultrasound compared with CT for intracranial lesions
John Lennon shot dead in New York

1981
Prince Charles and Lady Diana Spencer marry

1982
MRI scans described
Munchausen syndrome by proxy reported
Falklands War
American dentist receives mechanical heart

1983
Front seat belts in cars become mandatory

1984
AIDS virus is discovered
IRA bomb blasts Conservative Party conference in Brighton

1985
Live Aid concerts raise £40M for famine relief
Blood donations screened for AIDS virus

1986
Prevalence rates for fragile X syndrome reported
First transplant of heart, lung and liver

1987
200 die in *Herald of Free Enterprise* ferry
Tiananmen Square protests
Salmonella prevalence increases

1988
Measles, mumps, rubella (MMR) vaccine introduced
Government announces radical review of NHS

Preparation for and Birth of a College 1988–2000

The Presidents of the BPA during this period June Lloyd, David Hull and Roy Meadow, pursued the complexities of the formation of a College. David Hull attended the Privy Council to present the case for a college. No definite date for a decision was given and the process appeared to lie dormant. Members of the BPA were not aware of a secret battle that was being waged by opponents of the new college (see page 80).

David Hull reorganised the management structure of the Association to take account of the many new responsibilities for the BPA. A research unit was established in 1993 with David Baum as Director to develop and integrate the research, audit and surveillance activities of the BPA. The number of

publications of the BPA increased and included reports of working parties, drug bulletins, practice guidelines and books of historical interest. David Hall was elected Academic Vice President and Roderick McFaul became Health Services Vice President. During 1996 over 600 members of the BPA were contributing to activities and the membership had grown to 3300. Keith Dodd as Honorary Secretary drafted the charter for the new College which was finally granted by the Privy Council on August 23rd 1996. The designation Royal was approved on October 17th 1996.

Roy Meadow

Detailed recommendations for postgraduate training and regulations for continuing medical education were constructed by David Hall, David Davies and the Academic Board. The implementation of the Calman proposals for a unified registrar grade and allocation of these posts was undertaken by David Hall with the Regional Advisers. Graham Clayden was responsible for short and long term changes to the entrance examination for the Specialist Registrar grade to make it more appropriate for paediatricians.

The college purchased the building at 50 Hallam Street and moved there on November 8th 1997 from 5 St. Andrew's Place which had been the home of the BPA since 1985 but had become too small for the extensive activities. Incorporating the suggestions of many members of the College, the new Coat of Arms executed by the Royal College of Arms was presented at the first spring meeting of the College at York in April 1997 with Roy Meadow as the first President. The Princess Royal, the Patron of the College, attended a plenary session on the first day. Professor Sir Leslie Turnberg, President of the Royal College of Physicians of London was the guest speaker at the Annual Dinner.

Negotiations with the three other UK Colleges of Physicians resulted in an agreement that the entrance examination in paediatrics for the Specialist Registrar grade (MRCP) would be transferred completely to the Royal College of Paediatrics and Child Health. This change would enable the college to supervise the quality of entrants to the specialty as well as the training throughout the Specialist Registrar grade.

A strategy for the College was drawn up by Patricia Hamilton, Honorary Secretary, after extensive consultation with Members and Fellows (see page 86). A working party on advocacy for the child was formed. The Surveillance Unit with Christopher Verity as Director expanded the scope of the subjects assessed and the methods of the unit were applied internationally (see page 63).

The children of this country will enter the new century with a Royal College of Paediatrics and Child Health dedicated to fighting for the medical services they deserve.

1988–2000

1989
Surfactant available for clinical use
Hepatitis C virus discovered
Berlin wall demolished
Hillsborough disaster

1990
Hurricane batters southern England
NHS and Community Care Act
    becomes law

1991
Campaign to reduce the risk of cot
    death
Gulf War

1992
General Synod votes for ordination of
    women priests

1993
Calman Report on hospital staffing

1994
Mandela becomes President of South
    Africa

1995
Reorganisation of cancer services
Water restrictions after driest summer
    since 1659

1996
Royal College of Paediatrics and Child
    Health founded
Link between BSE and CJD established
16 primary school children murdered
    in Dunblane

1997
Labour elected for first time in 19 years
Diana, Princess of Wales, dies in Paris
    car crash

1998
Implanted artificial heart is effective
    for several weeks

Chapter 2: Portraits

Donald Court: A man of vision
AW Craft and DMB Hall

> We must continue to strengthen the foundations of paediatrics in the biology of development, extend our studies of the social determinants of health and disease in child and family, especially by the use of well planned local records; seek with psychology and psychiatry for a better understanding of the development of personality in the hope that we may find ways of diminishing maladjustment, excessive anxiety and destructive aggression in our children and parents: treat our patients with increasing skill and consideration and try, as honestly as we can, to overcome the dichotomy of treatment and prevention: establish these principles in the education of doctors and others professionally involved in the care of children.[1]
>
> Donald Court's 1970 Charles West Lecture,
> delivered to the Royal College of Physicians of London,
> entitled "Child Health in a Changing Community".

The 1970s were a time of consolidation and reflection for paediatrics in the UK. The specialty had begun to develop before the Second World War with many of the paediatricians having been primarily physicians who took an interest in children. Among the young enthusiastic doctors who came into paediatrics after the war was Donald Court. In the 20 year postwar period the organisation of the care of children had undergone a rapid expansion with paediatric units being set up in most major, and many smaller, hospitals. This growth was largely uncoordinated and there was a need to take stock. Donald Court took a leading role in this and was one of the most influential paediatricians of his time.

What were the sources of his greatness, of his depth, his integrity, and his humanity? He was born in Wem, Shropshire, the only child of a headmaster. His mother was the youngest of 17, so it is perhaps understandable why they stopped at Donald. One of his major early achievements was a school certificate examination in gardening of which he was most proud and which was to be clearly evident in the planning of his gardens in the future. However, he was not a practical man and left the execution of the manual work to others. It was once said "give him the job and he will finish the tools". Time, for him, was better spent in reading than changing a plug.

Court was greatly helped in his life and work by his strong Quaker philosophy. He came to Quakerism as a student and put the same degree of effort into this as he did to most other things in his life. Much of his thinking about the conflict between religion and science is encapsulated in two articles, published in 1965 and 1970, entitled "A scientific age and a declining church"[2] and "Leading a double life"[3] He was a 400 metre runner in his student days and this fleetness of foot and agility was constantly manifest in his future life, developing into a well-honed political ability. His advice to one young doctor embarking on a potential career in paediatrics was that the secret of success was to "keep both feet firmly planted in mid-air!"

After three years of dentistry he switched to medicine, qualifying in Birmingham in 1936. His early work at Great Ormond Street and the

Donald Court

Westminster Hospital was followed by the Emergency Medical Service during the Second World War and then to Newcastle as a Nuffield Fellow to work with Professor James Spence in his newly-formed department. This was a time of great opportunity and he joined a team which was planning the "Thousand Families" study in which he was particularly active between 1947 and 1954. The Thousand Families work and domiciliary visits led him to the homes of over 3000 families during his first 15 years in Newcastle and these clearly left a great impression on him and eventually led to the ideas first expressed in the Charles West Lecture. In 1950 on his return from the United States he was appointed Reader in Child Health and succeeded to the Chair in 1955 after the untimely death of Spence in 1954. He was indeed fortunate to follow in the footsteps of Spence, who had started the revolution in thinking on the care of children which Court successfully carried through.

Court's ideas were further developed in *Paediatrics in the seventies* which he wrote with Tony Jackson when they were Chairman and Secretary of the Academic Board of the British Paediatric Association.[4] He had a superb capacity to summarise and synthesise and he was in great demand as a chairman. It was no surprise, therefore, when Court was invited by the Secretary of State to bring together a group of individuals from all walks of life under his chairmanship as the Committee of Enquiry into the Child Health Services. Its report is universally known as the Court report[5] and bears his stamp on every page, written in beautiful English, quite unlike the verbiage of many such reports. It was full of compassion, clearly reasoned, and based on careful research.

That he brought out the best in people is exemplified by the words of Lady Jean Lovell-Davies:

> Donald Court would have liked to have had children representing their own views on the committee but fortunately for me he had to settle for parents. I was one of three parents chosen to put forward the views of users of the services. I had never previously sat on any sort of committee and, at the first meeting, was totally intimidated by the sight of a huge table with names in front of every seat, just like the ones I had seen on television reports of United Nations meetings. The feelings of foreboding and anxiety expressed themselves in giggles when I heard people using phrases like "through the chair" and other committee-speak. I would never have got round to making any contribution at all if Donald had not gone out of his way to ask what each parent representative thought at important moments in the discussion. He gave me the courage to speak and the belief that my views and the views of all children and their families were important.

He was greatly saddened and disappointed when it was received with less than enthusiasm by the medical profession and by the politicians who had commissioned it. In 1978 when Donald Court was being presented with the James Spence medal of the BPA the report was described by Otto Wolff as being a decade or so ahead of its time.[6] This indeed proved to be so. Court took quiet pride in seeing most of the report's recommendations being slowly implemented over the next 20 years even though his committee were never given any real credit. It had, however, clearly achieved its main purpose, to make the country, government, and profession more aware of the needs of children and how they had previously failed them.

Among the innovations were the establishment of multidisciplinary handicap teams, parent-held records, flexible training, and a career structure for clinical medical officers. However one of the main, radical proposals was that there should be an integrated child health service combining hospital and community care, with primary paediatric care being delivered by general practitioner paediatricians (GPP). It was the latter which engendered the most antagonism. He also foresaw the need for prevention to be given similar status to curative medicine.

There are several reasons why it took so long to act on the main recommendations of the Report. First, there were some real difficulties with Court's proposals. The distinction between primary and secondary care proved to be contentious and the costs were probably underestimated. Second, there were professional disagreements, both within and between disciplines, which hindered progress. However, by the late eighties there was an increasing consensus that primary care paediatrics belonged with primary care teams based in general practice and that doctors providing secondary care should be part of a unified paediatric department along with their hospital colleagues. The need for a more effective partnership between primary and secondary care was also accepted. The NHS and Community Care Act 1990 seemed to offer the long-awaited opportunity finally to unite community and hospital paediatric services across the country.

The concept of the GPP never found wide acceptance, for a number of reasons. First, while many GPs were, and still are, committed to specialisation within the primary care team, the idea of spending the bulk of their time with just one group of patients, defined by age, was contrary to their general philosophy of caring for the family as a whole. Second, the numbers did not add up – the idea might have worked in a large group practice but was likely to present real problems in smaller practices. Third, there was much debate as to whether a GPP could reasonably be expected to reach the level of skill in developmental diagnosis or educational medicine claimed by the community child health doctors, since a practice population would be unlikely to generate enough paediatric problems to maintain the skills of a GPP.

Donald Court always had a view outside of his own specialty and this was fostered when Spence encouraged him to take an interest in speech. This led to him being instrumental in setting up the Department of Speech Therapy in the University of Newcastle and he was also a prime mover behind the new Department of Human Genetics. He had a great ability to work closely with others and his collaborations with Issy Kolvin in child and adolescent psychiatry and Philip Gardner in virology were among the more notable. His work with the virologists was especially important in cementing the links between the largely clinical descriptions of respiratory illness from the past and the rapidly expanding scientific side, enabled by Gardner's pioneering work in rapid viral diagnosis.[7] Imparting his philosophies to medical students was seen as an important part of his life and he was not only an inspiring and popular teacher but also recognised the stress of medical student training and played a major part in the establishment of a personal tutor system. His recognition that much of paediatric care takes place outside the hospital was evident in the book which he edited, with the help of 12 local general practitioners, entitled *The medical care of children*.[8]

The health of children in the 1990s has been greatly influenced by Donald Court. He was a master wordsmith and his writings are a model of clarity and precision. He was always able to produce, at the drop of a hat, the apt poetical quotation, often from his favourites Auden and T S Eliot. On research it is perhaps worth quoting Court himself:

> Without continuing enquiry there is no progression. My plea is that we should apply the same critical energy to the study of social as we do cellular behaviour.

References

1 Court SDM. Child health in a changing community. *BMJ* 1971; **ii**: 125–31.
2 Court SDM. A scientific age and a declining church – what has a friend to say? *The Friend* September 1965.
3 Court SDM. Leading a double life. *The Friend* September 1970.
4 Court D, Jackson A. *Paediatrics in the seventies*. London: Nuffield Provincial Hospital Trust, 1972.
5 Court SDM. *Fit for the future*. Report of the Committee on Child Health Services. London: HMSO, 1976.
6 Wolff O. James Spence medallist, 1978, Seymour Donald Myneord Court. *Archives of Disease in Childhood* 1978; **53**: 609–10.
7 Gardner PS, McQuillan J, Court SDM. Speculation on pathogenesis of death from respiratory syncital virus infection. *BMJ* 1970; **i**: 327–30.
8 Court SDM, ed. *The medical care of children*. London: Oxford University Press, 1963.

Donald Winnicott

Donald Winnicott's contribution to paediatrics
JA Davis

Donald Woods Winnicott was the youngest child and only son of a Plymouth retail merchant who, as Lord Mayor of the city, was a close associate of its Members of Parliament, Lord and Lady Astor, and was knighted for his public services. His family belonged to the prosperous, unsophisticated, nonconformist West Country middle class whose culture was based on the Bible and on innocent domestic amusements. At the age of 13 he was sent to board at the Leys School in Cambridge and there became a close friend of Jim Ede, the founder of the Art Gallery in Kettle's Yard and curator of the Tate Gallery. Having decided to become a physician rather than to take over his father's business, he entered Jesus College as an undergraduate before completing his medical education at St Bartholomew's Hospital. He did not really enjoy his time at Cambridge; finding the focus on vegetative physiology and minute anatomy foreign to his own Darwinian concept of the human being as an integrated whole; and did not distinguish himself in the Tripos examination. He served as an unqualified medical officer in the Navy towards the end of the 1914–1918 war and for the rest of his life thought of himself as a survivor of the doomed generation while retaining much of its lost optimism and *joie de vivre*. He would recall with amusement the puzzlement of his fellow officers at finding themselves keeping company with an educated arriviste from what they thought of as the shopkeeping classes.

At "Bart's" Winnicott came under the influence of Lord Horder, whose insistence on good history-taking, he always said, formed the basis of his approach first to medicine, then to paediatrics, then to psychiatry. After taking up paediatrics he became the youngest consultant in London with appointments at the Queen Elizabeth's Hospital, Hackney and Paddington Green Children's Hospital and also to a number of LCC clinics as a result of which he became interested in the distinction between rheumatic and what became known as growing pains.

His paediatric textbook published in the early thirties is still worth reading as illustrating his holistic attitude to medicine and his awareness that, even then, much of a paediatrician's practice was to do with what he called psychosomatic conditions. The discovery of Freud and the experience of personal analysis, both as analysand and analyst, led to his moving from paediatric to psychiatric practice though even towards the end of his career he ran a clinic at Paddington Green at which allcomers were welcome and dealt with according to what their problems turned out to be. The Second World War found him running the very necessary psychiatric services for evacuees in Oxfordshire and in the course of this work he encountered, worked with and later married (his first marriage having broken down) the distinguished social worker, Clare Britton. At the end of the Second World War a series of broadcasts, directed to mothers of young children and later published, made his name almost a household word and phrases like "the ordinary devoted mother", "there is no such thing as a baby" and "the nursing couple" became common currency. Thereafter he was always in demand as a lecturer here, in the USA and in Europe, while his books became bestsellers in their field. This recognition, however, did not extend among his paediatric colleagues, and in the British Paediatric Association, though a member of longstanding, he remained something of an outsider, albeit he was elected President of the Paediatric Section of the RSM as well as of the Institute of Psychoanalysts and the American College of Psychiatry. The Squiggle Foundation remains as a Society devoted to the study and propagation of his ideas.

Towards the end of his life, although having himself practised both as a children's physician and a child psychiatrist, Donald Winnicott came to despair of any genuine rapprochement between the two disciplines (and indeed they now adhere to different medical colleges and seem to be going their separate ways) yet psyche and soma are inseparable in the infant and closely connected in the child. There are, of course, paediatricians who are aware that disease in childhood involves what Winnicott named the psyche-soma, but without education in developmental psychology, they tend to rush in where those with more experience would fear to tread, and in their enthusiasm may even gloss over those somatic aspects of a child's problems that it is their principal responsibility to deal with. Meanwhile child psychiatrists, as poor relatives of those who practice what has become the empirical psychiatry of adults, have to a degree lost touch with the developmental approach that should be their stock-in-trade.*

So what has been the legacy of Donald Winnicott to British paediatrics; that of a prophet not honoured in his own country or one whose psychosomatic approach is more honoured in the breach than the observance? What, of course, makes Winnicott suspect is his Freudian affiliations, the anathema of such high priests of scientific medicine as Sir Peter Medawar and – because he had reservations about some of Melanie Klein's formulations – unacceptable also to the bulk of child analysts. Winnicott's adherence to Freudian doctrine was, in fact, as a paradigm within which it was possible to frame and test hypotheses, rather than as a canon, but he persisted in attempting to understand what physicists call the hidden variables determining the apparently arbitrary behaviour of individual particles rather than adopting the statistical epidemiological approach exemplified by Rutter. These should not in fact be regarded as antagonistic but complementary. It would be futile and presumptuous of me even to attempt to summarise Winnicott's contributions to the theory of emotional development in this short article,† but I would like to draw attention to some which were essentially his own and which in my view represent his most important revision and expression of Freudian theory. They stemmed from the opportunity Winnicott had as a paediatrician to study prospectively those obscure reactions that are necessarily looked at through the wrong end of the telescope in the course of adult analyses – these early psychic events which according to the Freudian paradigm are major determinants of adult attitudes and hang-ups. While we now think we know that the mind of the newborn infant is not so much a *tabula rasa* as an exercise book with lines and headings, Winnicott was surely right in rejecting the caricature of attachment theory, which supposed that bonding was a fast-setting glue between the human mother and baby rather than a process of gradual consolidation – we are not ducks. On the other hand, he regarded the partial failure of such a developing bond as probably more important, if less obviously distressful, than to strain or even rupture it once formed by, for instance, admission to hospital or nursery, i.e. no or insecure attachment is more significant than temporary detachment. On the maternal side, he described a state of which he called primary maternal preoccupation – probably physiologically determined – which leads to most mothers narrowing their emotional focus to their baby late in pregnancy, at birth and

---

* As the late John Apley once memorably pointed out, this divorce has adverse effects on the children who are their joint responsibility.

† It took a whole book (*Boundary and space*, Penguin, 1991) for my late wife Madeleine to provide an adequate synopsis and critique of his always developing ideas.

until weaning, providing the setting for the reciprocity between mother and infant so cleverly explored by Professor Lynne Murray, Director of the Winnicott Research Unit. Failure of maternal adaptation very early in the baby's life Winnicott regarded as a deprivation that exposed the baby to traumata and that could result in psychotic anxieties. These ideas are important for paediatricians (and obstetricians) in organising maternity wards in such a way as to facilitate rather than impede such necessary and natural processes.

At the other extreme of infancy – after weaning – Winnicott described what he called a potential space between baby and mother which in psychic health could be regarded as imaginative play space in which the baby learned to use inanimate objects as a kind of halfway house between "me" and "not me". At the same time the baby becomes aware of his father as a wholly separate person, providing a model for the baby to use to establish "his" and his mother's individual separate identities. The coming together of those maternal aspects, which one could call fairy godmother and wicked stepmother on the Kleinian model, then leads to a capacity for depression as the baby struggles to reconcile hate and love for the same "object". In dealing with this situation playing becomes all important and is not to be confused – as written about by Winnicott – with, for instance, the gambolling of lambs. It will be appreciated that in Winnicott's view such psychic phenomena as psychotic anxiety, paranoia, and depression have natural and even useful biological roots rather than being regarded as pathological states of genetic or pathological provenance or due to brain damage.

Thus I identify five important concepts described by Winnicott with implications for paediatric medicine: primary maternal preoccupation, bonding as a process, the significance of human play and a fourth, outlined in Winnicott's best paper, fear of breakdown as a manifestation of a forgotten breakdown that has already occurred in early infancy, and, derived from Kleinian ideas, the birth of depression at the death of splitting as exemplified by the split between fairy godmother and wicked stepmother. Perhaps developmental paediatricians would also find useful Winnicott's simple method for testing the wellbeing of a baby that involved no more than watching his reactions to a metal spatula. The emotionally normal infant takes it only after hesitation while he makes sure that he has his mother's permission; the way he takes it is an index of motor maturity, as is whether he can or cannot drop it on purpose when tired of it; excited salivation when he puts it in his mouth shows whether he is capable of enjoying a semi-orgasmic oral experience from beginning to end; looking to see where it has fallen when he drops it is evidence that he has achieved the intellectual notion of object permanence. Such unstructured observation is more informative than a battery of formal tests in artificial circumstances.

What Winnicott practised was neither paediatrics nor psychiatry but the medicine of the psyche-soma during development. He would not have expected the physician in outpatients to attempt any kind of psychotherapy any more than surgery or other complex therapeutic procedures requiring referral to the expert, but he concurred with his friend and admirer Sir James Spence in regarding a properly conducted consultation as the basic element of medical care. It remains to be seen whether British paediatricians are ready and able to learn from him how their discipline can best be practised – rejecting the Cartesian dichotomy between physiology and behaviour, the vegetative and the animal aspects of our make-up. We are all, or should all be, Darwinians now, and just as anatomy is best understood through a study of embryology, the complexity of our minds is most easily understood in terms of psychic development. Winnicott's genius (it is difficult not to use that designation) lay not only in his ability to make brilliant conjectures about the nature of the psychological processes involved in the maturation of the human psyche – conjectures borne out when they have been tested – but in his extraordinary empathy with the feelings of children and their mothers. With him, theory and practice were indissolubly connected.

Profiles

The following pages contain profiles of paediatricians.

Sir George Frederic Still
1868–1941

Still was the leading paediatrician of the early part of the 20th Century and one of the driving forces behind the formation of the British Paediatric Association in 1928. He is, of course, best remembered by the disease that bears his name. While a medical registrar at Great Ormond Street Hospital in London he personally studied 19 cases of children with arthritis and wrote a paper which was presented on his behalf at the Royal Medical and Chirurgical Society in London in 1896. This study "on a form of Chronic Joint Disease in Children" was also the subject of his Cambridge MD thesis. His classic description included all of the major features that have become synonymous with this disease apart from the rash.

He was born in Highbury, North London, one of 12 children. His father was a Surveyor of Customs in the Irish Ports and the Port of London. Three of his siblings died in the first year of life, another aged 4 from scarlet fever and a sister of typhoid fever aged 18. He was the only surviving son and was brought up with six sisters. Frederic won a scholarship to Merchant Taylors' School and another to Caius College, Cambridge. His potential became obvious when he gained a 1st in the Tripos and was Winchester Prizeman. During this time he became fluent in Hebrew, Greek, Arabic and Latin. He qualified in medicine at Guy's in 1893 and then worked at Great Ormond Street as a registrar joining the honorary staff in 1899. In the same year he was appointed Assistant Physician for Diseases of Children at King's College Hospital. In 1906 he became Professor of Paediatrics at King's. During his distinguished career he wrote 113 books and papers including *The History of Paediatrics*. His literary efforts were not confined to medicine. He wrote at least two hymns and had a paper published in the *Journal of the Fly Fishers Club*. His retirement was spent fishing on the River Test. He did not marry.

Reference
Hamilton EBD. George Frederic Still. *Annals of Rheumatic Diseases* 1986; **45**: 1–5.

Sir James Calvert Spence
1892–1954

Spence, Still and Paterson were largely responsible for the establishment of the BPA in 1928. James Spence is remembered as a pioneer in the care of children in hospital who recognised the importance of the mother's role in helping to look after her sick child. Indeed his Babies Hospital, where mothers could "room in" with their babies, was a model that has now been adopted almost universally.

James Spence was born in Amble, Northumberland, the son of an architect, and qualified in medicine in the University of Durham in 1914 with an honours degree. War came soon afterwards and his efforts as a courageous stretcher bearer were rewarded with an MC. In 1924 he was appointed honorary consulting physician to the Babies Hospital and Mothercraft Centre where he undertook outpatient consultations as well as looking after 36 cots with babies and their mothers. Prior to the Second World War he undertook a study of mortality in childhood on behalf of the City Council. This led in 1947 to the One Thousand Families project with all babies born in May and June being entered into a prospective study. This was one of the first investigations to clearly associate poverty and ill health. In 1942 he was given the first University Chair of Child Health in England and founded the Department. Having been instrumental in setting up the BPA he then turned his attention to Australia which he visited on several occasions. Many paediatricians from Australia trained with him in Newcastle, and in 1951 the Australian College of Paediatricians was founded, much of the credit for it going to Spence.

He was an influential figure in British medical politics and administration being a member of both the University Grants Committee and the Medical Research Council. In 1950 he received a knighthood and in 1951 was President of the BPA.

Reference
Miller FJW. Sir James Spence, Professor of Child Health. *Journal of Medical Biography* 1997; **5**: 1–7.

Donald Paterson
1890–1969

Donald Paterson was born in Manitoba and graduated in Edinburgh. After two years with the First Dorset Regiment in France in the First World War, and a third as pathologist in the Canadian Army Hospital at Taplow he became a house surgeon at Great Ormond Street in 1919 and a consultant paediatrician there within a few years. He was responsible for the tremendous growth of postgraduate teaching which attracted doctors from all over the world. A man who worked himself and others as hard as Donald Paterson was bound to evoke resistance and his impatience sometimes limited his effectiveness. He recognised the importance of the laboratory but was sceptical of psychogenic factors in childhood illness. He wrote 60 articles, a textbook for undergraduates, a monograph on infant feeding and shared the editing of the leading British textbook of paediatrics.

His greatest contribution was the founding in 1928, with George Frederic Still and James Spence, of the British Paediatric Association. He was the Secretary for the first seven years, again during the Second World War, and President in 1947.

In 1947 he decided to return to his native Canada where he developed a new type of outpatient clinic which he called a "health centre" in Vancouver. In 1952 with government support he set up a comprehensive registry of chronic disease which became one of the most important information centres on disabling illness in childhood in the world.

Helen Mackay
1891–1965

While working as a young paediatrician in London, Helen Mackay joined a team from the Lister Institute that went to Vienna to study rickets in the famine following the First World War, which showed that rickets could be cured with cod liver oil and sunlight. Finding that many of the infants in Vienna were anaemic, she began to investigate the cause. After returning to London, to the Queen's Hospital in Hackney, she was the first to show the role of iron deficiency as a cause of anaemia in infancy and draw attention to its importance. Her study is the single most important landmark in our understanding of iron deficiency in infancy and also one of the earliest examples of a clinical trial involving medical statisticians.

Born in Inverness in 1891, into a family of Scottish minor gentry, Helen Marion Macpherson Mackay's roots were in the Highlands, but, surely, there was also something about her that could only have come from an education at Cheltenham Ladies College. She studied medicine at the London School of Medicine for Women (Royal Free Hospital) and qualified in 1914. In 1920 she was the first woman appointed as physician to the Queen's Hospital, Hackney and remained there until she retired in 1959.

Helen Mackay reacted to the poverty in the East End by taking paediatric care into the community, teaching about the impact of social conditions on child health and by leaning to the left in her political beliefs. She had a quiet voice and lacked small talk, but could be passionate in defending what she felt to be right and could show disapproval. Outside medicine, her abiding interest was ornithology. She loved to spend her holidays walking on the moors. She died of a stroke in the Elizabeth Garrett Anderson Hospital in 1965.

Her reputation rests on her major contributions to child nutrition but the deep respect in which she was held locally came from her unfailing commitment to her clinical work in the East End of London. Her achievements, together with those of other outstanding women doctors of her era, brought into focus the inequity of barring women from the male bastions of medicine. In 1934 she was the first woman fellow of the Royal College of Physicians and in 1945 she was one of the first women elected to the BPA.

Professor John L Emery

In spite of an Art Scholarship from school and pressure to go into the church John Emery chose medicine, qualified in 1939 and went into paediatrics. Pathology was then part of paediatric training. In 1947 he was appointed the first Consultant Pathologist to The Children's Hospital in Sheffield, where facilities were minimal, and when there were few children's pathologists in the world. He built up a Department of Paediatric Pathology that became known both nationally and internationally. It provided a comprehensive service closely linked to paediatrics – registrars worked for 6 out of their 24 months in his department – as well as teaching and research. Young pathologists came from many countries to work under him, learn from him and to do research. He established paediatric pathology as a specialty within the Royal College of Pathologists.

His main academic research arose out of the treatment of hydrocephalus and spina bifida where he did experimental work. His particular interest has been in attempting to estimate sufficiency of cause for illness and death. His work on infant deaths has resulted in the studies relating risk factors and the use of statistics in determining the risk of children dying. From this he has been involved in setting up preventive clinical programmes. He was also responsible for pioneering confidential enquiries on baby deaths which led to the DHSS Multicentre Study of 1984 and the more recent CESDI (Confidential Enquiries into the Study of Death in Infancy) studies. He played a major part in the setting up of The Foundation for the Study of Infant Deaths and the Developmental Pathology Society.

Those who know John Emery never think of him without his sketch book. At a meeting he will sit, apparently absorbed in what will be an excellent drawing of a speaker or a member of the audience, but, when comments or questions are requested, he will come up with a pertinent comment or penetrating questions. Suddenly, the meeting comes alive, ideas flow and everything is interesting.

Anthony Derek Maurice Jackson

As Secretary to the Academic Board from 1967 to 1973, BPA Honorary Assistant Secretary from 1973 to 1976 and Honorary Treasurer from 1978 to 1983 Tony Jackson has given longer service to the BPA than any other living officer. In addition, since 1983, he continued to assist the BPA in various ways including the manpower survey which has proved so important in assessing paediatric staffing requirements. He was co-author of *Paediatrics in the seventies*. For years he also served as the BPA's photographer and as such his 6 feet 3 inches interposed prominently but briefly between speaker and audience on nearly every important BPA occasion. He was made an Honorary Member in 1983.

He qualified from the Middlesex Hospital Medical School (1943) and from 1944 to 1946 served in the RAMC in Holland, Germany and North Africa. Paediatric training followed at the Middlesex Hospital, Great Ormond Street, the Queen Elizabeth Hospital for Children, the Institute of Child Health and the London Hospital. He was appointed to the latter and to St Margaret's Hospital, Epping as a consultant in 1959 and later (1965) also to the Queen Elizabeth Hospital. From 1970 to 1982 he was Postgraduate Sub-Dean of the London Hospital Medical College.

He was Chairman of the Paediatric Committee of the Royal College of Physicians of London 1975-1986 and a College Censor in 1980; President of the Association for Paediatric Education in Europe in 1986 and on the EEC Committee of European Societies of Paediatrics (1976-1985); President of the Section of Paediatrics of the RSM (1981-1982). He speaks three languages ranging from fluency to stuttering inarticulation and is such a good actor that after mimicking the cough of whooping cough to a student class he was invited to be President of the Student Dramatic Society.

Ronald Charles MacKeith
1908–1977

Ronnie MacKeith qualified at Guy's Hospital where he was house physician to the Medical Unit and then spent a year at Belle Vue Hospital, New York. He served in the Royal Navy from 1942-1945. In 1948 he was appointed Consultant Children's Physician to Guy's Hospital where he founded the cerebral palsy clinic which later became the Newcomen Centre for Handicapped Children. He encouraged undergraduates to think, argue and discuss and this earned him the label of an eccentric in the prevailing conservative hierarchical environment. He became Director of the Medical Education and Information Unit of the National Spastics Society (now SCOPE) and used his charm and skill to persuade professionals from different disciplines to attend short conferences where solutions to intractable clinical service problems could be mutually resolved.

In 1962 he founded the journal *Developmental Medicine and Child Neurology* which rapidly attained international stature. He was a gifted editor who saw the strengths and weaknesses of presentation instantly and was able to help authors to express their ideas more clearly. He was awarded medals or honorary memberships of many medical associations in other countries including the United States, West Germany and France. He founded the British Paediatric Neurology Association. His interest in psychosomatic medicine led to additional appointments as paediatrician to the Tavistock Clinic in 1950 and the Cassell Hospital in 1960.

Sir John Peter Mills Tizard
1916–1993

Peter Tizard was President of the BPA from 1982 to 1985 and in 1986 was awarded the Spence Medal. During his presidency the BPA was much involved in seeking to integrate hospital and community child health staff and in making the wider contacts which the expanding role of paediatrics, and therefore of the BPA, necessitated. In committee or in the chair Peter's forthright yet persuasive manner and ability to discount cant and humbug were used very effectively to the BPA's advantage. The establishment of the British Paediatric Surveillance Unit was largely his initiative. He continued as Chairman of its Scientific Committee after demitting office as BPA President.

He qualified from Oxford and the Middlesex Hospital in 1941 and after four years' service in the RAMC returned to pursue a career in paediatrics which led him to Great Ormond Street, St Mary's Hospital, the National Hospital for Nervous Diseases, Harvard Medical School and the Nuffield Institute for Medical Research in Oxford. In 1954 he was appointed Reader in Paediatrics and in 1964 Professor at the Institute of Child Health and Honorary Consultant Paediatrician to Hammersmith Hospital. At the latter hospital he established the Nuffield Neonatal Research Unit in 1961, a unit which pioneered studies on the scientific basis of neonatology and produced twelve professors. His talent for establishing a common sense of purpose and commitment in an environment of intellectual discipline was unequalled. Trainees and research fellows came from all over the world and many returned to run their own departments. In 1972 he was appointed to the newly created Chair of Paediatrics at Oxford, developing there the twin disciplines of neonatology and neurology.

His international standing was recognised by frequent invitations to give named guest lectures at home and abroad, and his corresponding or honorary membership of ten foreign paediatric societies. He was a recipient of the Dawson Williams Prize of the British Medical Association, President of the Neonatal Society and Master of the Worshipful Society of Apothecaries. He was knighted in 1982.

Baroness June Lloyd

June Lloyd was born in India, and lived there until she was 11. She came back to Britain with her parents, and went to school for the first time, at the Bath Royal School. She then went on to the University of Bristol to study medicine, graduating in 1951, and obtaining the MRCP in 1954.

June then became the first rotating paediatric registrar between the Bristol Children's Hospital and Plymouth. Following this she studied for a Diploma in Public Health in Durham, before moving to Birmingham where she developed her research and clinical interests in obesity, inherited lipid disorders and other metabolic diseases. She has a particular interest in abetalipoproteinaemia, and in preventing the fat-soluble vitamin deficiencies that occur in this condition. She also studied hyperlipidaemias in childhood, including the early detection and treatment of familial hyperlipoproteinaemias.

In 1965 she moved to the Institute of Child Health in London as Senior Lecturer, where she continued research into lipid and other metabolic diseases of childhood. At the same time she was active in teaching, travelled widely to lecture, and served on important national committees. During her tenure, she was promoted to Reader, and subsequently to Professor.

In 1975 she was appointed as the first Professor of Paediatrics and Child Health at St George's Hospital Medical School, London. For the first five years the academic department and laboratories were some miles from the clinical facilities, but her leadership ensured that clinical care and teaching were delivered to a high standard. The department flourished, and made significant research contributions over this period in nutrition, metabolic disease, problems of prematurity and growth, and childhood development.

June continued to be active nationally and internationally. In 1985 she was appointed Nuffield Professor of Child Health, at the Institute of Child Health, and the Hospital for Sick Children, Great Ormond Street. This brought new national responsibilities and challenges, including the Presidency of the BPA from 1988–1991. She retired from the Institute of Child Health in 1992, but still continued to work for the promotion of paediatrics, and for children's health care. In 1990 she was made a DBE and in 1997 Baroness Lloyd of Highbury.

Sir David Hull

David Hull has made outstanding contributions to the practice, teaching, and understanding of paediatric medicine in the UK. When he qualified from Liverpool University in 1953, paediatrics was a fledgling specialty. By the time he retired in 1996, he had helped child health become established as a specialty within hospital medicine, the undergraduate syllabus and the community, and had guided paediatricians into a new College.

After house appointments in Liverpool and national service in Berlin, he took up further training at Hammersmith and Great Ormond Street and was then appointed research fellow in Oxford. This was the beginning of his abiding interest in fetal physiology and the adaptation to newborn life. His initial interest was in brown adipose tissue and thermal control but he subsequently developed research interests in newborn skin, nutrition and placental transfer in addition to many clinical research projects, and published over 200 scientific papers. His prodigious research output continued throughout his career despite numerous other responsibilities.

After a further three years in Oxford as lecturer in paediatrics, he was appointed consultant physician at the Hospital for Sick Children, London. There he established a respiratory function laboratory and a reputation as a fine clinician. In 1970, he was offered the foundation chair in child health at Nottingham University, the first new UK medical school this century. When he arrived, there was no undergraduate course and a sparse clinical service. Perhaps his greatest contribution in a distinguished career was to create the lasting foundations for both. The undergraduate textbook, *Essential paediatrics*, written with Derek Johnston rapidly became a bestseller and it gave him great pleasure that it was adopted by most of the older medical schools.

David is a wonderful man. He was an inspirational teacher, a loyal colleague, a truly original thinker and a sharp clinician. There were very few conditions he had not seen. Although he could be a therapeutic nihilist, he was sceptical rather than cynical. His advice was constantly sought by numerous government bodies and professional organisations. He received many honours of which the presidencies of the Neonatal Society and the British Paediatric Association perhaps meant most to him.

Professor Edward Osmund Royle Reynolds

Professor Reynolds interrupted his medical studies at St. Thomas' Hospital to study science under Professor Henry Barcroft and Dr Maureen Young and qualified in medicine in 1958. For three years in the medical unit led by Professor Sharpey Schafer and in the paediatric wards of St Thomas' Hospital he enjoyed the challenge of putting clinical science into medical care. He learnt to take arterial samples and measure blood gases and published the results in the *British Medical Journal* and the *Journal of Pediatrics*. In 1962 he went to the Children's Hospital Medical Center in Boston and the Harvard Medical School as a Research Fellow. He met world authorities in respiratory physiology and neonatal care and studied the pathogenesis of hyaline membrane disease in lambs. He returned to England to help Professor Leonard Strang at University College Hospital establish a unit to study the fetal and neonatal lung. The unit published an outstanding series of studies on the pathophysiology of the developing lung and the adjustments that occurred after birth.

In 1965 when Reynolds was appointed lecturer in paediatrics, neonatal medicine was in its infancy and artificial ventilation had not yet been successful. He introduced and assessed new techniques for improving the survival of the newborn infant and for supporting infants with respiratory failure. He established a neonatal service which was considered the gold standard in the country. He was appointed Professor of Neonatal Medicine in 1976.

Professor Reynolds and his colleagues followed up all the infants under their care and reported the outcome. They studied recently developed imaging systems to devise methods to protect the developing brain. Collaboration with several departments, particularly medical physics, led to a series of papers on the value of ultrasound, nuclear magnetic resonance spectroscopy and near infrared spectroscopy in assessing the response to injury of the infant brain.

He acted as specialist adviser to the House of Commons Health Select Committee and was elected President of the Neonatal Society. He is a Fellow of the Royal Society which is a rare distinction for a paediatrician.

Sir Roy Meadow

Roy Meadow retired as Professor of Paediatrics and Child Health at St James' Hospital in 1998 after a distinguished career at Leeds University Medical School. He graduated from Oxford in 1960 and spent his early years at Guy's Hospital. After two years in general practice he returned to Guy's as a registrar in paediatrics. Here he studied the effects on parents of having a child in hospital. For this work on the "captive mother" he was awarded the BPA's Paterson prize in 1968. At this time he also developed his interest in paediatric nephrology. He then went to Birmingham where he studied the epidemiology of urinary tract infections in children before he was enticed to Leeds by Professor Smithells in 1970 as senior lecturer in paediatrics. Many medical students will have benefited from *Lecture Notes in Paediatrics* by Smithells and Meadow. When a second chair in paediatrics was inaugurated at St James' Hospital in 1980 it was natural that he should be invited to accept it.

In Leeds he initiated the paediatric nephrology service with interests as diverse as enuresis and renal failure. His clinical skills led to the description of what he called Munchausen syndrome by Proxy, but it is often referred to as Meadow's syndrome. His clear writing style made him a popular author of many texts. Under his editorship 1979–1987 *Archives of Disease in Childhood* thrived.

As a dedicated teacher of undergraduate and postgraduate students he was one of the first to recognise the importance of "teaching the teachers to teach". Many lecturers relate with awe their experiences of teaching students while the Professor made notes. His comments were always constructive.

A major contributor to the BPA, he served on Council in 1972 and on three further occasions. He was Secretary to the Academic Board and its Chairman 1990–1994 and was elected President of the BPA 1994–1997. At this time the drive for a College of Paediatrics was becoming unstoppable. Armed with a mandate from members of the BPA he pursued the target of a separate college which was attained in 1996. Roy became its first President.

He was knighted in 1997 for his services to child health.

Professor David Baum
1940–1999

David Baum qualified in 1963 at Birmingham. His early interests were in neonatal medicine, stimulated by five years at Hammersmith Hospital and consolidated at Oxford, where he was appointed lecturer and then reader, under Peter Tizard's founding professorship. His MD in 1973 was for work on retrolental fibroplasia (retinopathy of the newborn).

He invented the silver swaddler, used internationally in resuscitation and transport of newborns and developed the human milk pasteuriser, devices which have stood the test of time. In 1976 he was awarded the BPA's Guthrie Medal for outstanding research, by then increasingly in childhood diabetes.

In 1985 he was appointed Professor of Child Health at Bristol and, in 1988, became the founding director of its Institute of Child Health. The institute offers academic space for teaching, research by university or NHS staff and those from further afield. Uniquely, nested within it are many voluntary organisations; among the most successful is ACT, the Association for Children with Life-Threatening or Terminal Conditions and their Families, of which David Baum is President. Others, now freestanding, include Midders International, an evidence-based midwifery group, the music therapy group (now Music Therapy UK) and ERIC, the resource for families and professionals involved with enuresis.

From 1991–1995 David Baum was chairman of the British Association for Community Child Health and from 1993-1997 director of the BPA (later RCPCH) research unit. In 1997 he was elected President of the RCPCH.

His international child health interests started in Oxford with collaborative work in Thai villages, concentrating on infant nutrition; his Bristol project to develop Moscow's Filatov Children's Hospital led to Mikhail Gorbachev's honorary Bristol degree. In 1998 he started an RCPCH initiative to train paediatricians in Gaza, in the hope that peace could be furthered by a federation of national child health services.

He died, suddenly, in 1999 while engaged in a College initiative to raise money for children damaged by war. He was a man of great gifts who inspired and galvanised into action those whom he met or taught.

Bernard Valman

Bernard Valman graduated in medicine in 1958, having received his undergraduate training at Cambridge University and Westminster Medical School. After house posts and a period in National Service he held paediatric registrar positions in London, culminating in his appointment as Senior Registrar to Professor Otto Wolff at Great Ormond Street. In 1972 he became Consultant Paediatrician at Northwick Park Hospital.

A skilled clinician and thoughtful children's doctor, it was not surprising that he turned his attention early on to the organisation of children's services. He was prescient in recognising the importance of day care for children, assessment centres for children with disabilities, and the need for integrated child health services, concepts that he published and which attracted favourable attention. He has published many original scientific papers especially in the field of nutrition and gastroenterology in infancy, as well as stimulating and supporting the research endeavours of paediatricians in training. His natural ability to write simply and effectively led to his authorship of a number of books for parents, and the highly popular *ABC of One to Seven*, and *The First Year of Life*, books that have run into several editions.

His interest in scientific journalism led to his appointment as an Assistant Editor of the *British Medical Journal* from 1979 to 1982, and member of the journal's selection committee deciding the fate of submitted papers. Following this he accepted the challenge of Editor of the *Archives of Disease in Childhood*, a post he held from 1982 to 1994. He was instrumental in improving its scientific standard, and is now the Commissioning Editor, bringing new ideas to the review content of the Journal.

As well as holding administrative posts locally, including those of Clinical Director of Family Services and Children's Services, Dr Valman served as Secretary of the Paediatric Committee of the Royal College of Physicians of London from 1981 to 1991, and Chairman of the Examining Board for the Diploma in Child Health from 1984 to 1995. He is currently Honorary Archivist to our College, and was President of the Paediatric Section of the Royal Society of Medicine in 1999.

Professor Malcolm Leon Chiswick

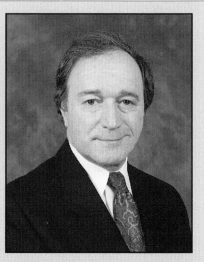

Malcolm Chiswick graduated in medicine at Newcastle upon Tyne and after registrar posts in Southampton and London became a research fellow in the Department of Child Health at St Mary's Hospital, Manchester. He became consultant paediatrician at St Mary's Hospital in 1975 and Professor of Child Health and Paediatrics in 1992.

His early research was on pulmonary surfactant, then on vitamin E and periventricular haemorrhage and the long-term growth and development of premature babies. His wide research interests included circadian rhythms, measurement of foot length in the newborn and, with obstetric colleagues, prenatal prediction. His extensive knowledge of the literature, sound clinical judgement and an ability to put important ideas into context made him ideal as leader writer for several journals. He is always forthright in tackling difficult subjects such as ethical problems or the provision of deficient resources. He has written extensively, particularly on perinatal events and outcome and has edited two volumes on advances in perinatal medicine.

Malcolm Chiswick became the first associate editor of the *Archives of Disease in Childhood* in 1985 when a new editorial structure was needed to reflect increasing specialisation in paediatrics. After two years, when he had proved the effectiveness of the new structure, he was appointed one of the twin editors of the journal. Additional associate editors were appointed to the *Archives* and this new editorial structure was adopted widely by other specialist journals. He launched the fetal and neonatal edition of the *Archives* in 1988.

He was a founder member, later Honorary Secretary, of the British Association for Perinatal Medicine and a member, later Chairman, of the joint committee of the British Paediatric Association and the Royal College of Obstetricians and Gynaecologists. He was Honorary Secretary of a Royal College of Physicians working party on neonatal medical services which produced an influential report. He served on the scientific advisory and medicolegal committees of the RCOG. During a critical period of the development of St Mary's Hospital between 1992 and 1996 he was Medical Director and Chairman of the management board as well as editor of the *Archives*.

Chapter 3: Development of paediatric specialties

Newborn care in the UK since 1928
PM Dunn

In 1928 newborn infants were in what John Ballantyne referred to as "no-man's land". Most obstetricians had become surgically-minded gynaecologists, while the 56 general physicians with an interest in paediatrics who founded the BPA were fully occupied with the problems of some 10 million older infants and children. Such care as was received by newborns, half of whom were born at home, came largely from midwives, nursery nurses and family doctors.

Into this vacuum stepped a young community medical officer, Dr Victoria Mary Crosse. In 1931 she was appointed by the Public Health Department in Birmingham to set up and run a unit for the care of premature babies. It was named Sorrento. Dr Crosse was a very disciplined lady, determined to salvage the many tiny infants who came to her from across the city. Infants were isolated, with strict control against cross-infection. Their temperature was closely monitored; the cots were heated by four hot-water bottles in canvas pockets, one being changed each hour. Careful attention was paid to the baby's nutrition with gavage feeding when necessary. The tubes were made of rubber and had to be removed between feeds. Later in the 1930s oxygen became available and also vitamin K. Other aspects of management included good records and, after the Second World War, audit of outcome at developmental follow-up. A voluntary transport system was also organised to collect the babies and later to return them home. In 1945 Crosse published her experiences in a slim volume entitled *The premature baby*. It went through many editions and was very influential in drawing attention to the needs of the newborn. Beryl Corner was the first general paediatrician to follow in her footsteps setting up a premature baby unit at Southmead Hospital, Bristol, in 1946 and developing an outreach team of health visitors trained in premature baby care. She also established a human milk bank.

Meanwhile in the 1930s and 1940s a number of general paediatricians were beginning to show an interest in the newborn baby. These included Charles McNeil of Edinburgh, Parsons, Cameron, Capon, Spence, Graham and Moncrieff. Waller published his monograph on breastfeeding. Some obstetricians and especially Holland and Baird were also making significant contributions.

The founding of the NHS in 1948 lowered the territorial boundaries between obstetrics and paediatrics. At the same time advances in understanding Rh haemolytic disease led to the appointment of resident paediatricians in major obstetric units to undertake exchange transfusions. Once they had gained entry to the neonatal nurseries they then involved themselves in many other aspects of newborn care.

The 1950s saw the pioneering of neonatal medicine – a term first used in 1960. In the early days there was no rooming in, few incubators, and hardly any technical equipment. Infants with birth asphyxia were resuscitated using intragastric oxygen. Infections posed a major problem, especially those due to the ubiquitous *Staphylococcus* and to *Monilia*. The antibiotics of choice at that time were penicillin, streptomycin and tetracycline. Exchange transfusions were a daily occurrence. All laboratory specimens had to be taken by venepuncture. Unfortunately, with little past experience and with grossly insufficient resources, many mistakes were made. In addition to retrolental fibroplasia, there was the grey syndrome and drug-induced kernicterus, and small babies were frequently starved for days to prevent aspiration pneumonia or allowed to become hypothermic. Cecil Drillien catalogued the sad outcome.

However, the tide was turning, aided by the research of a number of brilliant physiologists including Huggett, Barcroft, McCance, Widdowson, Young, Crosse, Hill, Strang and Dawes. These scientists further contributed by helping to train the next generation of neonatal clinicians. Paediatric pathologists such as Claireaux, Emery, Brown and Dawkins were also reflecting knowledge gained at necropsy back to the cot-side. Haematologists, including Coombs, Mollison, Walker and Tovey were improving our understanding of haemolytic disease, while in 1953 Ian Donald demonstrated the practicality of mechanically ventilating newborn infants. Pattle's observations on surface-active lung washings helped to pave the way for the eventual use of surfactant 25 years later. In 1958 Cremer observed the ability of light to reduce neonatal jaundice.

By the end of the 1950s an increasing number of general paediatricians might be identified as having a special interest in newborn care. In particular Tizard began to create a strong team at The Hammersmith. Other names include Mavis Gunther, Norman, Gairdner, Neligan and Oppé, while north of the border, the Scots could field, among others, Mitchell, Farquhar, Forfar and Walker. The decade also saw neonatal surgery being pioneered by Denis Browne, Isobella Forshall and Rickham. In 1959 clinicians, scientists, veterinarians and pathologists joined forces to found the Neonatal Society with a focus on fostering and reporting perinatal research.

Professor Sir Peter Tizard (1916–1993)

During the 1960s there was slow but steady progress with the establishment of special care baby units in major maternity hospitals. Technology arrived in the nursery with the Usher regime from Canada and the need to monitor acid-base status and blood gases and to infuse fluids intravenously. Appreciation of the significance of hypoglycaemia and polycythaemia led to the monitoring of blood glucose and the use of dilution exchange transfusion. Bag and mask ventilation, endotracheal intubation and mechanical ventilation became available. The management of the infant of the diabetic mother and of neonatal hypocalcaemic convulsions improved. Anti-staphylococcal agents such as hexachlorophane largely banished that troublesome organism from the nursery while nystatin proved to be a useful weapon against monilial infection. Newborn infants came to be properly examined at birth and screened for conditions such as congenital dislocation of the hip (Barlow) and for metabolic diseases such as phenylketonuria (Holzel). Screening for hypothyroidism, retinopathy of prematurity and deafness (Tucker) followed. Among other advances in the neonatal service at that time were the provision of chromosomal analysis and genetic advice, improved pathology and postmortem examination and the regular audit of perinatal outcome. Hull and Dawkins rediscovered brown fat. Amniocentesis, pioneered by Bevis in the early 1950s, led to Liley's method of assessing the severity of fetal Rh haemolytic disease and to the intrauterine transfusion. Later in the 1960s the work of Finn and Clarke led to the prevention of this disorder using anti-D prophylaxis. Other conditions such as phocomelia and rubella embryopathy were also disappearing, their place, alas, being taken by "new" diseases such as necrotising enterocolitis and gastroschisis. Many paediatricians contributed to the advances being made, among whom were Pamela Davies, Davis, Scopes, Robinson, Roberton and Baum, Strang, Normand and Reynolds, Dobbing, Barrie, Brown, Gandy, Campbell, Cockburn, Hey and Parkin, to name but a few. With encouragement from Nixon and Baird, perinatal epidemiology also came into its own with the reports of the 1958 British Perinatal Mortality Survey by Butler, Bonham and Alberman. This survey followed an earlier survey by Douglas in 1946. It was to be repeated in 1970 by Geoffrey and Roma Chamberlain.

Meanwhile technology was taking over the obstetric management of childbirth, with an increasing use of surgical induction, augmented labour, epidural anaesthesia, electronic fetal monitoring and operative delivery. On the doubtful assumption that no mother or baby should be denied the benefits of these techniques, more and more women were being delivered in hospital so that, by 1970, the percentage of home births had fallen from 50% to 13% and, by 1978, to 1%. Unfortunately there was a substantial lag in providing extra beds and staff to meet the new hospital demand, which put tremendous stress on the now overcrowded maternity hospitals. Slowly, during the 1970s, neonatal intensive care was developed in the main maternity hospitals. Although progress was hampered by shortage of staff and resources, there was tremendous support from the public. Great technical advances were taking place with the electronic monitoring of vital signs and of the infant's oxygen status, using first the intra-arterial oxygen electrode and then the transcutaneous oxygen monitor. Other apparatus that became available included infusion pumps, apnoea alarms, light therapy units, improved ventilators, methods for the delivery of continuous positive airways pressure (CPAP) and the equipment for providing parenteral nutrition (Shaw). Micro-methods for determining biochemical investigation, pioneered by Payne, at last obviated the need for venepuncture. These various advances permitted the successful management of < 1 kg infants, previously regarded as pre-viable. No group did more to further the care of the extremely low birthweight infant than that of Reynolds at University College, London. Ann Stewart undertook their developmental follow-up.

Many other new approaches to newborn care were introduced in the 1970s. One was an appreciation of the importance of involving the whole family in the exciting events around childbirth however ill the baby might be, and also of involving the mother in her infant's care. There was an increasing awareness of the importance of the social and emotional problems within a family and the need to support and counsel parents, especially when there was a bereavement. Once again there was a growing recognition of the importance of breastfeeding and human milk. At the same time there was an increasing interest in the ethics of decision making, particularly in regard to the withholding or withdrawing of medical care from babies with severe malformations or brain damage and those of extreme prematurity. The problem centred especially around infants with severe spina bifida. Enthusiastic efforts to treat these infants surgically in the 1960s had been disappointing. Mercifully the work of Smithells and others on the prevention of neural tube defects with folic acid eventually resolved this problem to a major extent. Mention should also be made of the pioneer work of Ian Donald using ultrasound which, with amniocentesis, opened up the field of prenatal diagnosis and genetic counselling and enabled more accurate assessment of fetal gestational age.

With the clinical advances of the 1970s came those of administration and organisation – new clinical records, protocols for management, improved developmental surveillance and more efficient methods of transporting sick infants. More and more there was collaboration between obstetricians, paediatricians and others in prenatal decision making and also in discussing outcome at regular conferences on perinatal mortality and morbidity. However, while these improvements were taking place in the major centres, progress throughout much of the country was slow, as the national statistics for perinatal mortality revealed. The problem was that neonatal care was still not recognised administratively by the NHS. The mother entered hospital as a single obstetric patient, and the fact that she went home with a baby under her arm was overlooked. There were budgets for the obstetricians and also for paediatricians based in children's hospitals but little for the newborn infant in between, unless they were admitted for special or intensive care. Ninety per cent of newborn infants remained in Ballantyne's "no-man's land".

During the 1970s there was a series of reports on neonatal care commencing with that of the Sheldon Committee (1971) which argued for regionalisation and a two-tier system of care. The BPA/RCOG Joint Standing Committee's report in 1978 proposed a more comprehensive three-tier provision of care and this was endorsed by the House of Commons Social Services Committee reports of 1980 and 1984. In 1982 the NHS set up a Health Service Information Committee under the chairmanship of Mrs Körner. This Committee recommended the identification of every newborn infant as an NHS patient with his or her own individual identity and record from birth. At last newborn babies achieved recognition, and with it came recognition over the next few years of the need for better staffing, improved facilities, and a neonatal budget.

Meanwhile another important development had taken place. In 1976 a small band of consultant paediatricians from the UK and Eire (who spent at least two-thirds of their time working with the newborn) met in Bristol and founded the British Paediatric Perinatal Group with the aim of improving the standard and provision of newborn care. Within a few years this Group had evolved into the multidisciplinary British Association of Perinatal Medicine (BAPM). Commencing with just 20 members, the Association is now 650 strong. Throughout the last quarter of the 20th Century it has worked closely with the BPA and the RCOG. Undoubtedly the most important achievement of the BAPM was to obtain formal recognition of the new sub-specialty from the Royal College of Physicians and the BPA. A Specialist Advisory Committee (Paediatrics) Training Programme was agreed in 1982 for those doctors seeking dual accreditation in paediatrics and perinatal paediatrics. The BAPM, at the SAC's request, also advised on guidelines for the recognition of hospital training posts suitable for those seeking such accreditation. Since 1997 the RCPCH has assumed responsibility for organising training in paediatric medicine and the BAPM has been invited to nominate specialty training advisors and members for the new College Specialist Advisory Committee in Neonatal Medicine.

A second BAPM objective is to improve the facilities for perinatal care. This aim has been prosecuted through national surveys on perinatal medical and nurse staffing, on the facilities for care of the newborn and in particular on the availability of intensive care cots, through advice to the DHSS and other national bodies and through published recommendations, such as the joint BPA/BAPM statement on Categories of babies receiving neonatal care. These important contributions have been enhanced recently by the publication of Standards for hospitals providing neonatal intensive care, defining the facilities and service specification needed to carry out high quality neonatal intensive care, and of the *BAPM dataset*, which provides recommendations for the collection of specific data to facilitate standardised annual reports for neonatal services. The Association has also furthered postgraduate education in perinatal medicine by holding regular national symposia and scientific meetings. Another aim has been to catalyse and organise multicentre research. In 1992 a Clinical Trials Group was established by Halliday and others in close conjunction with the National Perinatal Epidemiology Unit (Chalmers). Currently this Group is involved in 17 multicentre trials.

Returning to our survey of development, the pathological studies of Wigglesworth had done much to throw light on the haemorrhagic and ischaemic injuries to which the preterm infant's brain is prone. In 1978 Reynolds and his group reported on the use of ultrasound to scan the neonatal brain. A series of publications correlated the early ultrasound appearance with the later prognosis. In 1983 the same group reported on the use of magnetic resonance spectroscopy to investigate cerebral energy metabolism in the newborn and was able to show a derangement in infants suffering from hypoxic–ischaemic injury. From this research developed the concept of a delayed energy failure, thus permitting a window of opportunity for

Founding meeting of the British Association of Perinatal Medicine, Bristol, 1976. *Left to right: standing* – George Russell, Roger Harris, Niall O'Brien, David Davies, Colin Walker, David Harvey, Brian Wharton, Forrester Cockburn, Cliff Roberton, John Maclaurin, Richard Orme, Mark Reid, David Baum, Garth McClure; *sitting* – Pamela Davies, Osmund Reynolds, Peter Dunn, Margaret Kerr, Brian Speidel (in absentia: Malcolm Chiswick and Harold Gamsu).

treatment, an aspect under current investigation by Wyatt, Edwards, Thoresen and Whitelaw, among others. In 1986 Reynolds reported the use of yet another investigative tool, that of quantitative near-infrared spectroscopy which allows the measurement of a range of fetal and neonatal cerebral haemodynamic and metabolic variables.

The 1980s and 1990s have seen many other neonatal advances, including approaches to the prevention and treatment of the respiratory distress syndrome of prematurity using corticosteroids and surfactant (Halliday, Morley), the use of pain relief when appropriate (Anand, Aynsley-Green), and an appreciation of the importance of essential fatty acids for the normal growth and development of the human brain (Crawford, Lucas, Cockburn). Prostaglandin inhibitors, nitric oxide, anti-oxidants are among the new drugs that have become available, as has the technique of extra corporeal membrane oxygenation (ECMO) (Field). Elizabeth Bryan has done much to elucidate the problems facing twins, triplets and their parents. Their numbers increased dramatically with the introduction of new treatments for infertility (Levene). Doctors, if not mothers, have become more aware of the dangers of smoking and drug addiction. Neonatal nurse practitioners have made their appearance in the nursery (Hall). Regional organisation has improved with a more ready *in utero* transfer of infants likely to require neonatal intensive care (Fleming). Audit of perinatal mortality and morbidity has also become more refined, especially the long-term follow-up of very low birthweight infants (Cooke, Pharoah, Costeloe, Marlow). So many have contributed to these and other developments that it is not possible to name them all. However, along with those previously mentioned in the text (or in the caption on p. 47) the list should include Baumer, Cartlidge, Dear, Drayton, Dubowitz, Forsythe, Greenough, Hamilton, Holland, Hope, Johnson, Lloyd, Milner, Milligan, Modi, Morgan, Pearse, Rennie, Richards, Rivers, Russell, Tarnow-Mordi, Turner, Weindling and Wilkinson. Apologies are due to those whose names and contributions have been omitted in this brief essay, including many obstetricians, surgeons, pathologists, geneticists and others who have done much for perinatal medicine. Above all, recognition should be given to the many neonatal nurses who have contributed so magnificently to the care of the newborn and to both the maintenance and improvement of the service. A few years ago David Baum, President of the RCPCH, wrote: "Neonatal paediatrics is now the most rapidly growing and effective sub-specialty in paediatrics." It has indeed been an extraordinary success story with the current neonatal mortality reduced to a tiny fraction of what it was in 1928. But there remains a matter for concern. Many neonatal paediatricians understandably tend to focus their attention on the 10% of infants requiring special or intensive care. There is a real danger that the remaining 90% of infants (and their mothers), nursed in the postnatal wards and often returning home within hours of birth, may not receive the full attention they deserve. We must ensure that they do not return to Ballantyne's "no-man's land".

Surgery and anaesthesia
L Spitz and E Sumner

Paediatric surgery

The dawn of paediatric surgery in the UK occurred with the appointment, shortly after World War I, of Denis Browne at The Hospital for Sick Children, Great Ormond Street. He became the first surgeon in England to confine his practice entirely to children.[1] Other notable surgeons to follow included Isobella Forshall in Liverpool and Gertrude Herzfelt and JJ Mason Brown in Edinburgh.

By the early 1950s only a handful of paediatric surgeons existed in the UK. Together they formed the British Association of Paediatric Surgeons in 1953 with Denis Browne as their first Chairman and an Executive Committee consisting of JJ Mason Brown (Edinburgh), HH Nixon and DJ Waterston (London) and PP Rickham (Liverpool). The objectives of the British Association of Paediatric Surgeons (BAPS) were:[2]

a) the advancement of the study, practice and research in paediatric surgery
b) the promotion of the teaching of paediatric surgery, both undergraduate and postgraduate and advice on the training of paediatric surgeons
c) advice on matters concerning the paediatric surgical services in the British Isles
d) the promotion of friendship with paediatric surgeons overseas.

The BAPS was and remains the only truly international association of paediatric surgeons with a current membership of 918, of whom only 116 practice in the UK.

Paediatric surgery was recognised as a separate surgical specialty in 1968 when it received full SAC (Specialist Advisory Committee) status from the Royal Colleges of Surgery. The specialty has grown and expanded from its initial localisation in five centres, namely London, Liverpool, and Sheffield in England and Edinburgh and Glasgow in Scotland, to centres in every University Teaching Hospital as well as elsewhere.

The BAPS recommendation is that centres should ideally serve a population of 2.5 million and should comprise at least five paediatric surgeons, one of whom restricts his or her practice to paediatric urology. This concentration of expertise is necessary to maintain and advance the practice of and training in paediatric surgery and to carry out essential research and development to ensure the future of the specialty. The ideal paediatric surgical centre should, in addition to trained and accredited paediatric surgeons, be staffed by dedicated paediatric anaesthetists and should have close collaboration with the full range of specialist services for children including, specifically, neonatology and intensive care, oncology, radiology, and pathology. The nursing staff must be trained in paediatric nursing and, in the specialist areas, in paediatric critical care. Support services must cater for the specific needs of children including dieticians, social workers, play leaders and teachers. Access to the children, which used to be severely restricted, is now freely open with accommodation for parents available in many circumstances.[3]

Training in paediatric surgery has recently undergone a radical change. After completion of basic surgical training in surgery in general (minimum 2 years), trainees are required to complete a six-year programme in paediatric surgery of which one year may be spent in research, in an allied specialty or in training abroad. To obtain maximum exposure to a wide variety of experience, the training programme has been organised into six consortia in the UK and Ireland where trainees rotate through at least two centres during the five clinical years.

The era of rapid advances in paediatric surgical technology which characterised the 1950-1960s, has given way to more gradual progress with increased awareness of the special characteristics of perinatal physiology, advances in the sophistication of operative and anaesthetic techniques and improved pre- and postoperative care. The advent of intensive care with greater cooperation between neonatologists and paediatric intensivists and the provision of safe parenteral nutrition have been major advances. For example, survival rates of infants born with oesophageal atresia have improved from 62.8% in the period 1951–1959[4] to 87.6% in 1980–1992.[5] For duodenal atresia mortality has decreased from 49% between 1951–1965 to 5% in 1981–1995 while hospital stay has reduced from a mean of 35 days to 18 days in the same time periods.[6]

The aphorism of Sir Denis Browne that "the aim of paediatric surgery is to set a standard not create a monopoly" has gradually evolved so that neonatal surgery has become the monopoly of the paediatric surgeon. This applies equally to the surgical management of infants and children with complex conditions requiring special expertise, to the management of relatively straightforward surgical conditions in children who have an associated disorder, and to complex paediatric urology.

There remains a significant proportion of general paediatric surgery that is carried out by general surgeons in district general hospitals. The range of procedures include relatively common disorders that do not require a major operation or complex perioperative care. The conditions include elective procedures such as hernia, hydrocoele, circumcision, orchidopexy and emergency operations for appendicitis in the older child, torsion of the testis, irreducible inguinal hernia and minor trauma. This contribution is recognised by BAPS, who in conjunction with the Senate of Surgery have advocated a minimum period of six months training in paediatric surgery for general surgeons undertaking paediatric surgical practice.

The paediatric surgeon also has a major part to fulfil in the counselling of parents in whom a prenatal diagnosis of a congenital abnormality has been made on antenatal ultrasound scanning. Accurate information of the likely outcome for the infant as well as the place, method and timing of delivery are major considerations for the paediatric surgeon. The place of prenatal intervention remains to be established but at present the practice is confined to specially designated research centres to prove its value.

The areas of organ transplantation and minimally invasive surgery have expanded rapidly in recent years. Graft survival following kidney, heart and liver transplantation is currently over 80% while the results of intestinal transplantation are encouraging. Many invasive abdominal and some thoracic procedures can now be performed endoscopically with decreased pain and more rapid recovery. Its role in paediatric surgery remains to be defined.

Advances in chemotherapy with close collaboration between the oncologist and paediatric surgeon have brought about dramatic improvements in survival of patients with solid tumours (over 80% for Wilm's tumour, 70% for hepatoblastoma) whereas the Stage 4 neuroblastoma rate remains relatively fixed at around 25% despite intensified chemotherapy and major biological research efforts. Advances in tumour biology should improve the outlook for Stage 4 neuroblastoma in the future.

Paediatric Anaesthesia

In most developed countries, paediatric anaesthesia has become a recognised sub-specialty with infants and young children referred to specialised centres where their unique requirements are managed. Several studies including Keenan *et al.* and the NCPOD report from the UK have shown that mortality and morbidity in young children may be greater if treated outside specialist centres by nonspecialist anaesthesia and other staff.[7,8]

The first textbook of paediatric anaesthesia was published in 1923 by Langton Hewer who pointed out that children's requirements are different and that anaesthesia may be more challenging than for an adult. The T-piece circuit was described by Ayre in 1937 and subsequently modified in the 1950s by Jackson Rees of Alder Hey Children's Hospital in Liverpool who was one of the great founding fathers of the sub-specialty.

The Association of Paediatric Anaesthetists of Great Britain and Ireland was founded in 1973, now with UK and foreign members it has been the model for many other national societies. The international journal, *Paediatric Anaesthesia* (Blackwell Science) was started in 1989 with affiliations to all the important associations of paediatric anaesthetists in the world.[9]

Care of the patients has changed over the years with parents being fully involved and informed at all stages of care, including induction of anaesthesia and recovery. One of the advantages of the anaesthetic room, still used in the UK, is that the parents can easily come into the area even in street clothes to be a support to their child.

More premature babies and those with complex problems are surviving because of the growth of neonatal and paediatric intensive care and newer therapies including surfactant, respiratory and cardiac support, which is often complex (e.g. high frequency oscillation, ECMO, use of nitric oxide etc.) and total parenteral nutrition (TPN), together with nursing and medical expertise. The ex-premature baby who needs a hernia repair is a modern challenge for the anaesthetist as there is a continuing risk of apnoea, bronchopulmonary dysplasia and oxygen dependency. Certainly, the close relation of anaesthesia and the growth of PICU has widened the scope of surgery for sicker patients and with improving results.

Intense interest in postoperative and procedural pain relief was stimulated by the work of Anand and others in the 1980s who demonstrated that many children suffered pain either because it was thought that small children did not feel pain or the staff were nervous of the respiratory side effects of opioid drugs if given to small babies.[10] Analgesics written "IM prn" were often simply not given. Topical local anaesthetic creams (EMLA, Ametop) mean IV puncture is no longer painful and can also be used e.g. for pain relief after circumcision.

The first acute pain service for children in the UK started in 1990 for research into and treatment of postsurgery pain and that associated with medical conditions such as sickle crisis and allowed acute pain to be dealt with on an individual basis.[11] Major pain is managed by epidural infusions, via a catheter, of a mixture of local anaesthetic agent and an opioid (usually morphine) or intravenous or subcutaneous morphine infusions as patient controlled analgesia (PCA) or nurse controlled analgesia (NCA) using specifically designed syringe drivers. NCA is particularly successful as the nurses like to be involved and relies on a low-level background infusion with a bolus of drug administered as necessary by the nurse, but with a "lockout period" of 20 minutes for safety. Regular clinical monitoring of vital signs and a simple pain and sedation scale are the key to success. A child who has mastered a computer game is suitable for PCA. Newer analgesics such as the non-steroidals are used, often rectally, either on their own or as a morphine-sparing device. Paracetamol is freely used now we realise its safety, even in the newborn. In the older infant a starting bolus can be as high as 50 mg/kg if given rectally. The IV injectable prodrug, propacetamol is in use in some countries, though not in the UK at the moment.

Regional anaesthesia, combined with light general anaesthesia is nowadays a routine part of anaesthesia and extends into a pain-free early postoperative period. It includes the use of regional and central blocks, such as epidurals, caudal and spinal and stems from early enthusiasts in the 1980s in centres in France, Italy and the UK. The techniques carry a very low morbidity and have been extended, with the use of long-term catheters for acute and chronic pain relief.

Over the years a great deal of new equipment has been introduced, especially for respiratory support and monitoring, e.g. pulse oximetry has become a universal non-invasive monitor for all stages of anaesthesia and recovery and provides crucial information on oxygenation and the circulation. In paediatric anaesthesia, where patients can desaturate with frightening speed, this monitor is invaluable.

Many new drugs have been adopted by the paediatric anaesthetists from the adult field. Hitherto, children have been "therapeutic orphans" with many commonly used drugs such as fentanyl, bupivacaine, midazolam, propofol and dopamine never having a product licence for use in children. Now the FDA and other agencies require phase 3 trials to be undertaken in children where appropriate. Sevoflurane, a new inhalational agent underwent such trials and is now in widespread use as an induction agent for children, being pleasant, nonpungent, rapid (48 secs to loss of eyelash reflex) and cardiostable.

Newer agents tend to be shorter acting and benefit ambulatory patients, but there are increasing numbers of reports of emergence delirium even in children who are pain-free. Perhaps it is better for small children to wake up slowly.

Many challenges face the paediatric surgeon and paediatric anaesthetist in the next millennium. The role of prenatal intervention needs to be evaluated. The place of minimally invasive surgery requires to be defined. Amelioration of the stress response and effective measures to prevent sepsis will undoubtedly improve the results of neonatal surgery.

References

1 Rickham PP. Denis Browne: surgeon. *Progress in Paediatric Surgery* 1986; **20**: 69–75.
2 Swain VAJ. *The genesis of the British Association of Paediatric Surgeons*, 1981.
3 Spitz L. Neonatal surgery. *JR Coll Surg Edinb* 1995; **40**: 84–7.
4 Waterston DJ, Bonham-Carter RE, Aberdeen E. Oesophageal atresia; tracheo-oesophageal fistula. A study of survival of 218 infants. *Lancet* 1962, **ii**: 819–22.
5 Spitz L, Kiely EM, Morecroft JA, Drake DP. At risk groups in oesophageal atresia for the 1990s. *J Pediatr Surg* 1994; **29**: 723–5.
6 Murshed R, Nicolls G, Spitz L. Duodenal atresia: 40 years' experience (submitted).
7 Keenan RL, Shapiro JH, Kane FR, Simpson PM. Bradycardia during anesthesia in infants. An epidemiologic study. *Anesthesiology* 1994; **80**: 976–82.
8 Lunn JN. Implications of the NCPOD for paediatric anaesthesia. *Paediatric Anaesthesia* 1992; **2**: 69-72.
9 Sumner E. Paediatric Anaesthesia. *Paediatric Anaesthesia* 1994; **4**: 1–2.
10 Anand KJS, Sippell WG, Aynsley-Green A. Randomised trial of fentanyl anaesthesia in preterm neonates undergoing surgery: effects of the stress response. *Lancet* 1987; **1**: 62–6.
11 Lloyd-Thomas AR, Howard RF. A pain service for children. *Paediatric Anaesthesia* 1994; **4**: 3-15.

Developing community child health, paediatrics and child public health
A Macfarlane

Where on earth did "community" paediatrics arise from? It certainly had no well demarcated birthing point, but has rather appeared like a photograph being washed in developer, gradually defining itself over the years. It still awaits the fixing process and has, as with so many developing processes within the NHS, been carried out in virtual darkness. (Well, there may have been a little red light somewhere around to help us vaguely visualise what was happening – but not much!) However the more the developing process continues the more appears on the "positive" – evidence-based child preventative health and health surveillance, child public health, hospital at home, multidisciplinary care of disabled children, child protection, acute assessment centres, combined working.

If there had been a defined starting point of doctors working in the community for the health of children, it is lost way back, even before the establishment of the National Health Service, before the school health system, before even the emergence of health visiting as a profession during the late 19th and early 20th centuries. Does it even matter when or where it began? Probably only to a historian. What matters to the contemporary child health worker is the direction in which it has developed recently, so as (a) to help better understand whether or not it now meets the relative health needs of children, young people and their families, and (b) to make some rational prediction as to how it should, and will, develop in the future. The present worry is that even if you were to show our developing picture of community paediatrics and child health to the average general practitioner working in a Primary Care Group, a glazed look of incomprehension might well creep over his or her face.

As more and more different aspects of the service take on defined forms, does the work involved in community paediatrics and child health make up any cohesive whole, other than the fact that the work is mainly concerned with (a) the health and illness of *individual* children and young people up to 16 to 18 years of age outside of the hospital setting and (b) the health and illnesses in *whole populations* of children? The answer is "probably not". Why? Essentially this is both because services should respond to need (and the health and illness treatment and management needs both of individual children and whole populations of children are constantly changing) and because there are never enough resources to manage all these needs, so that priorities have to change too. The delivered services have to reflect these factors.

To ensure that at least in one area we are all talking the same language, what definition should we put by the term "health" in context here? The closest suitable definition is provided by Professor Lennart Kohler in his paper "Child public health" published in the *European Journal of Public Health*:[1]

health is the ability to resist the strains and stresses of a physical, mental and social nature, so that they do not lead to a reduction in life-span, function or well-being.

Let us return to the dark room and examine the presently developing snap. Central to the picture there is now emerging clearly a colossus of a figure cupping a child in his or her protective hands, each finger of which is marked. The first reads "the preventative care of children", the next "the long-term care of children with disabilities", a third "the care of sick children at home", a fourth "the protection of children" etc. There stands that ubiquitous, marvellously adaptable and on the whole, increasingly well-trained professional; yes – the parent – stalwartly continuing the perpetuation of his or her genes and the human race, mainly unacknowledged in this, their key role, by the likes of politicians, the tabloids and many doctors (except when some poor parent can no longer cope with the unrecognised burden of their child-rearing existence, and manages notoriety by doing damage to their gene bearers).

Some scenes are also better developed than others. To the left of centre stands a multi-headed hydra named "child health surveillance". Facing this monster is a highly esteemed professor who, with head surrounded by a halo proclaiming "the pen is mightier than the sword", is steadily chopping off the hydra's (screening) heads with a clutch of reports. The all encompassing "routine check" monster appears nearly slain, a few heads remain, others, like "screening for growth problems" are re-growing, but even as we watch, behind the harassed professor now emerges a legion of new angels in T-shirts reading "The National Screening Committee".

A further scene, surrounded with a glow of success, is of characters from the Department of Health, working hand-in-hand with basic scientists and local community child health professionals (parents, health visitors, general practitioners, community children nurses, community paediatricians and others), sticking highly effective vaccines into children. In some areas, this scenario, from time-to-time, still gets blurred with natural concerns, but the "feeling" of the scene as a whole is hugely positive.

Another central vista is of a vast gleaming billion pound hospital with two doors. Out of one streams a line of happy children into the arms of their smiling parents. Over this door is a concrete Chairman Mao like figure, in his right hand a volume of biblical proportions inscribed "The thoughts of the hospital care specialist". Out of a smaller side door there rolls the occasional child in a wheelchair, supported on a home ventilator and cradling an oxygen cylinder, into the outstretched arms of sad, depressed and ever-tired parents, held up as they collapse from fatigue by a small group of supporting carers one of which has an armband marked "community paediatrician". A speech bubble is visible, appearing from his or her mouth. If you reach for your magnifying glass you will see the words, directed at the image of his hospital colleague, saying "I know that we are working at this together but are you absolutely sure this is always in the best interests of the child and family or is it because you are so determined and proud of your technology?"

If we look again at the supporting figures surrounding the parents of the disabled child, it is clear that they are beginning to work in cooperation. Further, the number of emerging figures is increasing; with the community paediatrician are therapists, health visitors and community children's nurses, general practitioners, and representatives from social services, education and the voluntary organisations. Within the group, a camaraderie is obvious. This is much needed, as the children appearing from the hospital building have increasingly complex handicapping conditions and the parents are looking more and more fatigued. However it can be seen, as the picture develops further, that a point will be reached where the question appearing in the speech bubble will grow and grow and become a shout from the parents and all those working with these seriously disabled children and their families in the community – "Enough, enough. There is a limit to which technology should be used. Where are the ethics, where the sensitivity, where the humanity?"

This message for the new millennium from this particular scenario will have to be that if money continues to be spent on technologies for keeping severely disabled children alive, the money must also be *guaranteed* for supporting these children within their families at home and, where necessary, outside of the home, so as to ensure that the "care" factor is as important as the "technology" factor. Arguments about the *balance* of resourcing will run and run. (Like now, there will in the future never be enough to adequately resource them both.) Further, in this brave new world, all new technologies in neonatology will hopefully be subjected to rigorous, randomised long-term trials, before being allowed any prospect of general usage.

How high a profile does "preventative care" have in this emerging picture and, where there is evidence of effective preventative care, does community paediatrics have a major role? Immunisation of children remains the single most cost effective intervention available. (Triple vaccination holds the record at a massive 14:1 ratio.) The vaccines have been developed over the years by a wide variety of doctors, scientists and others. The recent role of the community paediatrician has been as part of a team ensuring that the vaccines reach as many children as possible. What of "health promotion" in the field of child health? Is it a "dummy" sold to us by politicians, who could no longer hide the fact that socio-economic inequalities were the single major factor in health differences between individuals within populations, but who still needed a way to be appearing to be doing something without attempting to equalise the distribution of our gross national product (in case it lost them votes)? "Yes", is the simple answer, though in spite of the money wasted on health promotion there are a few interventions that are effective. But these pale into insignificance compared with the failures. Social class inequalities in standardised mortality ratios at all ages are increasing; there is an increasing number of children living in families below the poverty line, smoking rates among young people are increasing. The list goes on and on.

So what do we now hope will emerge clearly in the field of community paediatrics and child health over the next twenty or so years? First and perhaps most important is a better defined idea of what the overall paediatric services, both in the community and in hospitals, will look like. How will community paediatrics and hospital paediatrics combine and integrate? The most rational way will be by developing the concept of *all* paediatricians having the same basic training; a training which should include at least a grounding in "child public health" and the concept of health for whole populations of children. During this training, and most appropriately at specialist registrar level, *all* paediatricians will be trained further in some specialist area – community child health, child public health, cardiology, endocrinology, intensive care, or whatever. Though here it is envisaged that "community child health", the clinical care of individual children outside of hospital, will begin to develop as a specialty separate from "child public health", the care of total populations of children. This will happen at least partly because professionals with child public health training will come from a variety of different backgrounds both within medical and nursing training, and from outside, epidemiology, service planning, management etc.

How will paediatricians with a special interest in community child health and their colleagues with a special interest in say cardiology or endocrinology, work together in the future? Some of the following will be inevitable:

- in district general hospitals (DGH) without paediatric inpatient facilities (where smaller paediatric inpatient units will no longer be viable) paediatric services will consist of assessment centres open during the day only. These will support general practitioner referrals, accident and emergency department referrals, local outpatients for children, simple procedures such as X-rays and blood taking. They will be run by community paediatricians with a special interest in community child health. The services of these paediatricians working in these DGHs will also be required by primary care groups and trusts for organising and coordinating the local secondary level care services for all children with special health needs living in the community (including children in need of protection)
- in district general hospitals with inpatient facilities, paediatricians with a special interest in community child health may, in the future, be on the "on call" rota with their hospital-based colleagues, may have a role in helping to run the accident and emergency departments, and will be responsible for the organisation of the "hospital at home" services. They will also have to respond to the needs of primary care groups and trusts and be responsible for organising and coordinating the local secondary level care services for all children with special health needs in the community
- in large tertiary care paediatric centres with teaching responsibilities, it is less and less likely that paediatricians with a special interest in community child health will feel adequately trained to be "on call" but they will,

on the other hand, be most likely to provide, for general practitioners, the closest to a "general paediatric" advice during normal working hours. In place of being relieved of the "on call" responsibility they will take on a greater teaching role in medical student and CME training, while remaining responsible for organising and coordinating the local secondary level care services for all children with special health needs in the community.

Within this developing scenario the greatest challenge will be the management of children's accident and emergency so that the most senior, as well as the most junior paediatricians are at the front door of the hospital. At the present time, in the majority of these establishments (but not all) there remains a singular failure of seniors to be there, in A and E, to assess and offer experienced advice on children referred by general practitioners, as to whether a child should or should not be admitted, and to offer appropriate support to parents and teaching to the juniors. It may be that consultant paediatricians with a special interest in community child health working in large DGHs and tertiary care centres are in the best position to provide this expertise, given that they may have the broadest knowledge of general paediatrics and will have intimate knowledge of the community facilities which the child may be supported by should they be able to be cared for at home. Hopefully with primary care groups and trusts controlling the secondary care budgets and the commissioning of secondary services, they will continue to push for this change.

Turning to the "total population" role of paediatricians and others trained in "child public health", a main feature of this will be advocacy on behalf of children and young people. It is a role which both the Royal College of Paediatrics and Child Health, and other relevant organisations are only just beginning to develop. However it must be seen as not only important but absolutely vital, given that the voice of children and young people, until now, has been weak, particularly in the UK. In this advocacy role, child public health professionals and the relevant organisations will need to use the UN Convention for the Rights of the Child and one of its key statements, that of ensuring that the child's own voice is heard.

Further, those involved in child public health will be needed to support the changing commissioning world of primary care groups, advise on health matters across all the different services both within and without the NHS, and develop a European perspective in child health matters. The child public health remit will be to improve the overall health outcomes of whole geographical groups of children using a wide range of tools including national and local politics, better overall coordination of all services related to child health, liaison between health, social services, education and non-governmental organisations at strategic planning level.

So perhaps the "developing photograph" metaphor will now have to be changed. It is not flexible enough. It cannot cope with the rapidly changing picture, the need for flexibility, and the need above all for community paediatrics and child health to work increasingly with other services in a mutually respectful, supportive and communicative way to the better health needs of children, young people and their families – most essentially in support of the colossus "child health worker" of society, the parent.

Reference

1 Kohler L. Child public health: a new basis for clinical health workers. *Eur J Pub Health* 1998; **8**: 253–5.

Child psychiatry
M Lindsay

There have always been some children who have been disturbed and distressed. In this country, until the first quarter of the 20th century, there were no facilities or psychiatrists specifically for children.

In 1920 when The Tavistock Clinic opened, the first patient was a child, but most were adults. In 1923 The Maudsley Hospital opened and their outpatients included children – Sir Aubrey Lewis believed all psychiatrists should be able to treat children. Later each had their own Children's Department.

Emmanuel Miller, who played such an important part in the development of child psychiatry here, recognised that children's conditions were different and nearly always needed to be treated along with parental problems. In November 1927 he was the psychiatrist at the first place in the UK that dealt specifically with children – the East London Child Guidance Clinic, run by the Jewish Health Board, and working mainly in the evenings with volunteer helpers.

In 1928 The Child Guidance Training Centre opened, a clinic for demonstration and training, where the psychiatrist, social worker and psychologist worked together as a team, along the lines developed in the United States for delinquent children, possibly seen to be in greater need of treatment than neurotic children. The team approach has become the pattern for child psychiatry since then, though the description "child psychiatry" was not used until 1933.

During the 1930s similar clinics were established, always characterised by lack of agreement as to what should have been set up. During the 1939–1945 war children's emotional disturbance, away from home and family, alerted people to the need for such services, even if they were less than perfect.

After the Second World War local authority Child Guidance Clinics or Child Psychiatry Departments in hospitals became available in most parts of the country. The team approach was broadly similar in both. The psychiatrist had not then had much training. The London School of Economics educated psychiatric social workers from 1929 till recently. The psychologists brought to the clinic their immense knowledge of child development that had accrued since the end of the 19th century. Other disciplines joined the team, including, in some cases, child psychotherapists.

Therapists may have been a useful luxury, but most clinics saw that psychodynamic thinking was particularly applicable to children. It is incorporated into all aspects of practice and used by all disciplines often unwittingly. It extends assessment and treatment and justifies psychological interventions.

Teaching and research

Analysts contribute to the understanding of children's difficulties. Melanie Klein, who came to Britain in 1926, was a child analyst. Her theories influenced Winnicott, and are the basis for the training of child psychotherapists at the Tavistock Clinic. Anna Freud came here in 1938, analysed children but also worked in cooperation with teachers and parents. She too learnt much about separated children during the War at her Hampstead Nurseries. In 1947 she started the Hampstead Child Therapy Course. One of her interests was the effect of illness on the emotional life of children and she met with paediatricians to discuss their cases. Her writing is clear, and her classification clarified emotional delays in children. Donald Winnicott, a paediatrician who became an analyst, gave talks and wrote about children's developmental needs and difficulties, and how he communicated with them – by drawings and listening very carefully, lessons which were useful to child psychiatrists. Margaret Lowenfelt used play, often in a sand tray, to enable children to tell her about themselves.

John Bowlby's works on attachment, separation and loss are fundamental. Further work, for instance by Mary Ainsworth, has enabled an assessment of attachment in children to be made – avoidant, anxious and ambivalent – from which some idea can be gained as to the quality of care the child may have had. James Robertson, working with Bowlby at the Tavistock Clinic in the 1950s, filmed the effect of separation of the child from the mother in hospital, and also in a children's home and in foster care. The films led to an awareness of the child's need for the mother in hospital, and it became routine for her to stay. The films also changed the way young children are looked after when away from parents and in the care of social services.

Michael Rutter's research has included work on the classification of the conditions from which the children suffered: conduct disorders, neurosis, and psychosis. His classic epidemiological studies showed for example, problems in a normal population, and the variation in different places – poverty makes parenting more difficult – and the great importance of school. He looked at the effect of sick parents, head injury and deprivation in children, at the importance of both nature and nurture in the origin of disturbance and is working on the nature of resilience.

Research now is less broad, being more concerned with a particular condition. It is of a high standard and more academic departments of child psychiatry are needed. Every teaching hospital should have one.

Methods of working

In the community-based child guidance clinics, and the hospital-based child psychiatry departments, the way of working was much the same. Originally the child was seen by the psychiatrist, and the mother by the psychiatric social worker, who tried to help her sort out the problems which got in the way of her parenting. Subsequently fathers were included; the staff found they were doing marital work.

Then in the 1960s family therapy emerged (though Emmanuel Miller had probably practised it). There were hopes that the waiting lists might disappear, which of course they did not, though it was useful treatment and of benefit to many families. Family interaction becomes clearer – the difficulties children and parents have with each other, the way that rewarding children get better care than those who are unrewarding and how scapegoats arise in families – which may lead to abuse and neglect. Increased sophistication, one-way screens and videos of the meetings, seen by the family, have improved both assessment and treatment.

Behaviour therapy, cognitive therapy and short-term psychotherapy and various forms of groups have all become treatment options available in many clinics. Drugs are increasingly used in adolescence. In children methylphenidate is given for accurately diagnosed attention-deficit hyperactivity disorder.

Working and consulting with other agencies is a major part of the work. These might include, for instance, social services, who look after the most disturbed children in the community, or health visitors, who are involved with young children and prevention of future problems. All clinics have too much work, and there is always a hope that consultation may reduce referrals. Even if it does not, it prevents the family having to see more people.

Specialisation is increasing, but the child guidance clinic, like the paediatric department in a district general hospital, has to leave that to the teaching hospitals, which also provide a tertiary service.

Teaching has always been a feature of child psychiatry. Now that child psychiatry is needed for general psychiatric training, and community child psychiatry is needed for specialist training, specialist registrars often become part of the team. Trainee social workers and psychotherapists are other members. Specialist registrars in child psychiatry have a specific training programme supervised by the Royal College of Psychiatrists.

The Children Act of 1991 has meant that child psychiatrists have increasingly been asked to help the court decide what is in the child's best interests. This could itself be called a form of treatment.

As the work changed so did the name. Various titles are now used such as Family Consultation Service or Child and Family Psychiatric Service.

Interestingly, a recent local poll showed that general practitioners and the families preferred the name Child Guidance.

Trends for the future

For about 30 years following the Second World War, services increased. Day units and inpatient units for children were opened, as were adolescent units. However, in the succeeding 20 years it has become increasingly difficult to increase the staff level, though this does not stop the number of patients increasing. In addition the team has become vulnerable; the psychologists moved out to other premises, social workers are paid by social services, who want the clinic or hospital social workers working with them.

In the 1990s the need to know the outcome became important, and clinical audit is now necessary. It is sometimes quite difficult trying to put rather abstract improvement into concrete figures. It concentrates the mind on what has been done, and adds to staff stress.

Paediatricians and child psychiatrists work together better and "liaison psychiatry" has emerged. There has been some mutual scepticism in the past. In reality, the two disciplines complement each other. If shared training is introduced, understanding of the other might improve. However they are different disciplines and different cultures, as families find when they move from one to the other. Paediatricians have to be prescriptive; child psychiatry tries to enable families to find ways of sorting out their problems. It was once suggested the two disciplines should "get married for the sake of the children". It would not have worked. Now each discipline has a college, for which examinations are required for membership.

In 1962 Ronald MacKeith, an astute observer of the child psychiatry–paediatric scene, organised a debate at the Paediatric Section of the Royal Society of Medicine, between Sir Aubrey Lewis, who believed child psychiatrists should come from psychiatry and Donald Winnicott, who maintained they should come from paediatrics. It could be said the debate continues.

Over the last half of the 20th century the population of children and adolescents has increased, as has their emotional disturbance. The staff in child psychiatry departments have recently decreased and so the impact that they make is much less. It is hard for administrators, with no money, to improve the situation, even though the service is so essential for the future of the nation.

Chapter 4: Achievements of the BPA

The British Paediatric Surveillance Unit
EM Ross and R Lynn

Rare disease and infections are, by definition, individually uncommon, but collectively they are an important cause of morbidity and mortality in childhood. The British Paediatric Surveillance Unit (BPSU) was set up in 1986 to perform research in this area. Through the simple methodology of circulating monthly report cards the Unit has enabled paediatricians in the United Kingdom and Eire to participate in the surveillance and further study of uncommon disorders affecting children. The undertaking of nearly 50 projects by the Unit has produced a major British contribution to practical medical epidemiology.

History

The BPSU arose from a number of pressures operating in the early 1980s. While the British Paediatric Association (BPA) was growing rapidly through consultant expansion, simultaneously the Communicable Disease Surveillance Centre (CDSC) of the Public Health Laboratory Service (PHLS) in London, headed by Dr Spence Gailbraith, wished to develop a system to speedily recognise and monitor newly recognised infectious disease. Gailbraith (rightly) surmised that paediatricians as a group would be fruitful to approach. There was good reason to believe this. Paediatricians had already been involved in a card reporting system in the 1960s when helping to collect data for a study of lead poisoning encephalopathy, undertaken by Professor Donald Barltrop and colleagues at St Mary's Hospital. This methodology was adopted by the National Childhood Encephalopathy Study co-directed by Professor David Miller and Dr Euan Ross at the Middlesex Hospital Medical School. In the course of three years consultant paediatricians reported 1182 cases of infant encephalopathic disease.

The early 1980s saw passive reporting of Reye's syndrome, haemolytic uraemic syndrome, Kawasaki disease and haemorrhagic shock encephalopathy syndrome to CDSC by paediatricians. However, it was felt that rates might be understated, so active surveillance was considered.

Discussions were held in 1984 between, what were to be the parent bodies of the BPSU, the BPA, PHLS and the Institute of Child Health (London). A small steering committee later to be known as the BPSU Executive Committee (BEC) under the chairmanship of ex-president of the BPA, Sir Peter Tizard was then set up. Sitting on the BEC were the three parent bodies along with representatives from the Faculty of Paediatrics of the Royal College of Physicians of Ireland and the then Communicable Disease Surveillance Centre of Scotland. The BEC considered how best to implement active surveillance using the methodologies previously developed. It was felt that the introduction of such a system would allow for the increased ascertainment necessary for assessing trends in rare disorders. Such a system would reduce the number of requests for data received by clinicians from individual researchers.

The objectives of the BPSU were to facilitate research into uncommon childhood disorders, for the advancement of knowledge, to allow paediatricians to participate in surveillance, to increase the awareness within the medical profession and to respond rapidly to public health emergencies. From the outset it was agreed that simplicity was to be the watchword. The BEC of today still takes these principles to heart.

In July 1986 the first BPSU orange card, listing the names of six disorders (AIDS, Lowe syndrome, haemolytic uraemic syndrome (HUS), neonatal herpes, subacute sclerosing panencephalitis (SSPE), X-linked anhydrotic ectodermal dysplasia) was dispatched to 800 consultant paediatricians in the UK and Ireland.

Administration

Now as then, the BEC consists of paediatricians and clinical epidemiologists who are drawn from the wide range of disciplines that make up paediatrics. Much of the original success of the Unit can be laid at the door of Dr Susan Hall, consultant epidemiologist, and Myer Glickman, administrator, who implemented the wishes of the committee. Currently there are two medical advisers, Dr Angus Nicoll and Dr Jugno Rahi and a scientific coordinator, Richard Lynn, reflecting the increased workload of the Unit. The committee meets monthly to discuss proposals and to consider the future direction of the Unit. In 1995 the BPSU became part of the newly established College Research Division, which encompasses surveillance, research and audit. The activities of the BPSU are discussed at the yearly Research Division Advisory Committee.

At its outset the BPSU was aware that it could not be a financial burden on its parent bodies. Throughout its history the Unit has endeavoured with success to be self-supporting. The past President of the Royal College of Physicians, Sir Cyril Clarke, was instrumental in obtaining a grant from an anonymous Trust. A long association with the Children Nationwide Medical Research Fund followed. Currently the Unit is supported by a grant from the Department of Health (DoH), which recognises its contribution to public health in the UK. Further funding is raised through the monthly contribution of £210 by each study using the system. The unit also recognises the uncosted contributions of the time and effort made by the parent bodies.

Methodology

The Unit's office is housed in the offices of the Royal College of Paediatrics and Child Health (RCPCH) and is run by the scientific coordinator, Richard Lynn and his assistant Myra Schehtman. Each month all those participating in the scheme, currently 1920 clinicians, are sent an orange reporting card listing the conditions currently under surveillance. To avoid burdening clinicians, a maximum of 14 studies are placed on the card. A set of instructions for completing the card, including the case definitions of the conditions is also circulated.

Respondents are asked to return the card to the BPSU office, indicating the number of cases of each condition that they have managed during the preceding calendar month. Scottish paediatricians return their completed cards via the Scottish Centre for Infection and Environmental Health. An important feature of the system is the returning of the cards even if no cases are seen. This allows the monitoring of compliance. In the year 1997 93% of cards were returned monthly. Once the BPSU office is made aware that a clinician has seen a case, the researcher undertaking the appropriate study is informed. They then contact the clinicians to collect the relevant data; over 90% of these requests are completed. Since its inception over 12 000 cases have been reported.

In the main, though the Unit initiates some projects, it exists to facilitate the research interests of RCPCH members. Following an initial enquiry, those wishing to place a condition on the card receive a package of information to help them develop an outline proposal. If the draft proposal appears suitable for incorporation within the BPSU, it then seeks a more detailed application. Much of the development of the application is undertaken through discussions with the BEC's medical advisers. The Unit often invites applicants to one of the monthly executive meetings so that the proposal can be discussed. In this way they get a clear idea if the proposal is suitable or not. The Unit repeatedly asks "what are the research questions and will surveillance answer them?"

Though many of the projects undertaken have been from major academic units some have been from individuals in small units. The Unit has fond memories of the chemistry set poisoning study successfully completed by Tom Mucklow of the Isle of Wight. The data contributed to a change in the legislation relating to children's toys.

Achievements

In its achievements the BPSU has surpassed original expectations. Not only has the Unit supported research workers in the study of rare disorders but also the outcomes have had substantial impact on public health. As early as 1986 the BPSU was monitoring the effects of new warnings about aspirin and Reye's syndrome. The Unit has kept under surveillance diseases targeted by vaccination programmes as well as late sequelae. Examples include the surveys on congenital rubella, meningoencephalitis after MMR vaccine, acute flaccid paralysis and Hib vaccine failures. The Unit has provided the base for reporting HIV and AIDS in children in the UK and Ireland. To achieve this it has cooperated with obstetricians, laboratories and others to give maximum surveillance coverage. One of the aims of the Unit is to have rapid response to emergencies. Here the Unit helped assess the impact of changing the route of administration of vitamin K to newborn infants, following concern about a possible link between vitamin K injections and the subsequent development of childhood cancers. Recently the BPSU has been involved in monitoring new variant Creutzfeldt Jacob disease in children (through the Progressive and Intellectual Neurological Disorder survey) and of *E. coli* 0157 outbreaks and their impact on the level of haemolytic uraemic syndrome.

Further achievements can be seen in the educational role the Unit has played, through the production of an annual report, a newsletter, over 100 publications and presentations and the holding of national conferences, seminars and workshops. The Unit also now has its own web site (http://bpsu.repch.ac.uk).

The success of this methodology has encouraged adoption by other medical specialties within the UK e.g. ophthalmology, neurology, gastroenterology, dermatology and occupational health medicine. Ten other paediatric surveillance units have developed abroad including Australia, Germany, Netherlands, Switzerland, Papua New Guinea, Malaysia, New Zealand, Latvia and Canada and, nearer home, in Wales and Ireland. Many of these units have now linked to form the International Network of Paediatric Surveillance Units. This network intends to increase communication between research workers, develop standardised research protocols, promote and develop new national units and undertake surveillance on a global basis.

Conclusion

The BPSU started sending out its orange reporting card in 1986. It is a well established part of British paediatric practice and now has its place in the history of epidemiology. Over the past two decades the BPSU has met and exceeded the aims set by its founders, principally by keeping to its original principles of robust simplicity. In maintaining this approach we hope that it will continue to act as a global model for developing child health epidemiology.

As Sir Cyril Clarke said in 1991: "British and Irish paediatricians therefore feel justly proud of themselves as the pioneers and key enactors of this unique reporting system".

Finally, special thanks should be given to all those who have contributed to the running of the Unit; those mentioned previously and past chairmen, Professors David Baum and Catherine Peckham, advisers Drs Ruth Gilbert and Margaret Guy; all those who have sat on the Executive Committee, those who have financially supported the Unit and its projects and the paediatricians and medical specialists who have reported cases and given their time to complete questions.

Medical education and training in the 1990s
DP Davies

Naturally conservative, we are bewildered by the rapidity of a forced progress and change . . . we have outrun an education system framed in simpler days for simpler conditions.

Sir William Osler, 1913

I was Chairman, first of the Academic Board of the British Paediatric Association (BPA) and then of the Royal College of Paediatrics and Child Health (RCPCH) 1994–1997. These were eventful years when a national programme for Continuing Medical Education (CME) was launched, when syllabuses and training records for General Professional and Higher Specialist Training were, with full consultation, written and made available to trainees and when there was a special recognition not to consider the undergraduate years of education in isolation to the rapid changes that were taking place in postgraduate training. In Britain, we are in the midst of a remarkable cultural revolution in medical education and training – red guards of change at all levels are still very active. I often wonder if things were really as bad as some thought to justify all this activity!

Undergraduate education

Encouraged by the General Medical Council's (GMC) *Tomorrow's doctors* (1995) all medical schools in Britain are changing their undergraduate teaching programmes, embracing the new concepts of core syllabus and special study modules – "that part of the course which goes beyond the limits of the core and that engenders an approach to medicine that is constantly questioning and self-critical" (GMC). Some of these changes are radical, introducing problem-based learning – along the lines, for example, of those from McMaster, Maastricht and Newcastle (New South Wales) – from almost the first day in medical school. Most have embarked on more integrated curricula with clinical medicine introduced earlier, ethics and communication skills assuming greater importance than in traditional curricula and from an early stage, basic sciences made more relevant to their clinical application and, in general, the creation of a more receptive learning environment encouraging, especially, the driving force of individual curiosity. These major changes continue to place huge demands on medical schools and, collectively, district general hospitals, community trusts and general practices which, it is all too often forgotten, provide significant amounts of clinical teaching away from the main teaching hospital base. Paralleling these changes in curriculum content have been new teaching and assessment methods, with modularisation far more a part of assessment and with much less emphasis on the "big bang" type of final MB. Medical schools have also had to ensure continued excellence in delivery of their traditional curricula as they have been gradually phased out.

However, it has been disappointing, in contrast to the five year cycle of research assessment in universities, how little extra money has been forthcoming to implement these changes. In Britain, much as somewhat belatedly, we like to think we are beginning to value teaching and training more, sadly, sufficient financial support has not yet arrived to secure these new educational ideals – a theme I return to later. This is an urgent matter to address, especially with the increased student numbers that now have to be accommodated in British medical schools. Will all these changes to undergraduate curricula be worthwhile? Was the old system really that bad? Only time will tell.

Admission to medical school

Mention must also be made of the selection of medical students for university. It is remarkable how much fog has surrounded the selection of medical students until comparatively recently. But the Dearing, Woodrow and McManus Reports have placed special emphasis on widening access to higher education and the worry of discriminatory actions of medical schools as they affect the admission of students from ethnic minority groups and other disadvantaged areas of British society. A transparency of the selection process that was often previously all too opaque is demanded now. Obligations under equal opportunities law must be respected to allow medical schools to reflect the social structure of the population as a whole, more than they do now. Any hint of discrimination must be removed. At the same time there is concern about the new gender imbalance that has crept into medical student selection. Now, for a variety of reasons, far more women are admitted than men, sometimes with ratios as high as 70:30. The situation now is as unhealthy as it was when men were over-represented, if we look ahead at the not inconsiderable implications for later health service planning. The detriment to boys in comprehensive schools serving disadvantaged parts of the country is also as important. All these issues rightly widen the debate on discrimination and disadvantage in access to medical schools beyond the current concern about the more traditional issue of racial discrimination. To get the right mix of talent entering medical school that better reflects our society is important for arguments both of equity (everyone having a fair chance) and for the future pattern of health care delivery. If doctors are better informed about inequalities in health, coming, as many will do, from areas of disadvantage and high in health need, then, so the argument goes, perhaps they will see a greater need to provide improved services in these areas of increased risk and help to drive change. Many hundreds more medical students will be needed to staff medical services, with less reliance on doctors trained overseas. As another part of the argument for widening access, should more graduates enter medical school to boost these numbers? If so, can and should they be fast tracked? Innovative pilot schemes have already started to look at some of these issues.

What this current debate on student admissions reminds us is that, for those involved in the wide continuum of medical education and also in the later delivery of service by the products of this system, we can no longer deny the importance of recognising that it all begins with the admission of young people into medical school. We should be better informed about selection processes and, where possible, involve ourselves in them.

Continuing medical education

Let us now move to the other end of medical education and consider Continuing Medical Education (CME). In 1995, Wales and the South-East Thames region undertook a pilot study for the Academic Board of the British Paediatric Association, introducing a scheme for CME for all career-grade paediatricians. Five years on CME has come to seriously occupy our thoughts. But the idea of continuing education is not new. The written word is almost as old as time itself; symposia, workshops and lectures are all well-established means for updating our knowledge and skills, with patient-centred discussions on ward rounds, a unique source of updating ourselves and generating new ideas. But we were then told that what was needed was a more formal structure not only to keep us abreast of new knowledge and to maintain and improve the quality of our clinical practice but also so that the public, increasingly better informed about medical matters, could see that we were taking continuing competence seriously; if, as a professional specialty, we did not do this ourselves, it would, sure as not, be imposed on us by some outside authority. The CME programme is now in its fifth year. There are signs that, however doubting the Thomas" might have been initially about its value, there is now an ever increasing variety of activities being proposed for CME. Opportunities to interact with experts outside an individual's own domain, national and regional meetings, symposia and workshops organised by our specialty groups, self-directed activities and meetings, journal clubs, case presentations, courses in apprenticeship activities, are but some examples of a rich tapestry of continuing learning opportunities out of which 50 hours per year need to be credited. Let us not forget also that a couple of hours spent with an expert in an outpatients clinic is probably much better than many hours sitting in a lecture theatre. Yes, there were worries. Some found it all a waste of time to cater for (so it was held) less than 5% of doctors who made no effort to keep up-to-date. But with clinical effectiveness and clinical governance becoming increasingly important, continuing education has assumed a gravitas that was less evident at its conception. An important spin-off, which has particularly impressed me, is that CME has provided opportunities for those less fortunate doctors (especially CMOs, SCMOs, staff grade doctors) who before were rarely provided with educational opportunities, to further their postgraduate education and training. There is a long way to go but initiating CME has acted as an important catalyst for these doctors.

A greater public demand for doctors to maintain their clinical competence will lead inevitably, to some form of re-certification. As it stands at present the College, which supports, supervises and administers CME, is likely to rule that a list of those who have completed a five year programme of 250 CME credits will be published after its Annual General Meeting in 2002. But the question remains: how do we judge the success of structured CME, just as how do we measure changes at the beginning of the process in new undergraduate curricula? These are important concerns but almost impossible to answer. I have a simplistic response: that it can only be in everyone's best interest to be on top of our subject, to plan for particular gaps that we have and simply get on with it. Individual doctors will trivialise the CME commitment at their peril. But, as I write, CME itself as a basic concept is also evolving into CPD (Continuing Professional Development). This recognises that not only is updating of skills and knowledge needed but also that this must be woven into other aspects of our professional performance, including management and other personal attributes involved in the delivery of health care. We are now being encouraged to organise for ourselves a cycle of personal development, where the needs for the year are planned, rather than, as so often happens, keeping up-to-date on an opportunistic basis.

General professional training

Between the extremes of undergraduate learning and CME is the meat of our education and training sandwich which we are so radically changing – General Professional Training (GPT) followed by Higher Specialty Training (HST). A new look into the content of this training was long overdue when it was considered by the Academic Board of the BPA in the early 1990s. The first edition of a *Syllabus and training record for general professional training in paediatrics and child health* was published in 1995, by Dr David Thistlethwaite (Consultant Paediatrician in Blackburn) and myself, using a format that had been originally piloted in Wales a couple of years before. A major consultation exercise had taken place with all the specialist groups, Regional Advisers and other key people involved in training, to create a syllabus that reflected contemporary paediatrics and child health. It is remarkable how the introduction of a postgraduate training syllabus came so late in the day. Why aims and objectives, well established for student learning, were deemed less so for postgraduate and clinical training is a mystery. Unfortunately, some of the "great and the good" held the opinion that medicine was a subject too big for doctors to have such a curriculum! It is almost as if we were above it all. For trainees, what was now offered was a syllabus and training record to work from, instead of the haphazard and serendipitous dipping into paediatric texts. Protected time for training was to emerge. The concept of "learning moments" was conceived, with a variety of learning opportunities having to be offered during the working week. Consultants, on whom most of this education will fall, could relax! They were not to spoonfeed but to act as educational facilitators. What we had to do was to provide a rich educational culture medium in which self-directed learning ideas could germinate, providing, of course, that the training paediatrician could be rescued from shifts and reduced hours of working to benefit from this learning. Noble ideals, indeed, but often difficult to deliver, as we have learnt by now. But in all this we must not forget how much can be learned at the bedside, clinic and surgery – the "coal face" of medicine – not a bad apprenticeship for clinical medicine, at one time the envy of many parts of the world. Indeed, we have to be careful to ensure that the phoenix rising from the ashes of traditional learning will not die prematurely. There is a wonderful laboratory of learning through patients who have real problems with a real need to be resolved, embracing a complex mesh of real psychological interactions. This is a concept of service-based learning that was not discovered by modern day educationalists, as some would have us believe. It has always been with us. But what we are now talking about is complementing this core with other learning methods, carefully planned using the Syllabus and Training Record, to help steer the learner through the maze of ill health of children in all its therapeutic, preventive and social dimensions.

We are also learning that having a syllabus to follow is one thing but knowing how to use it is quite another. Doctors in general (including consultants) are not used to using a syllabus and keeping a record of their learning. We all have a lot to learn about implementing a syllabus. I have also held that this generally agreed syllabus should be the core of that for the examination that assesses the level of knowledge and clinical competence, completes the general professional basic specialist training phase and provides the entry into higher specialist training, the MRCP. This itself is also undergoing change to accommodate the changing attitudes to learning.

Higher Specialist Training

Higher Specialist Training (HST) is a minimum of five years. The Calman Report in 1992 envisaged that doctors would spend a shorter time training and it was to maintain and improve the standard of this training that better structure and supervision was indicated. HST also required syllabuses which were published in 1996 (coinciding with the implementation of the Calman Report in paediatrics) for each sub-specialty training programme in child health, including general paediatrics – also considered a specialty. As with GPT, our specialty groups were very much involved in formalising these syllabuses and similar teething difficulties were experienced. How our current trainees receive this level of education and training varies enormously throughout Britain and is under the control and direction of regional HST committees. As in GPT, core service-based learning is complemented by specific learning and training programmes in protected time, including study leave provision. The first two years consolidate and develop what has been learned in GPT. Log books, assessment procedures and annual reviews before moving on to the next phase are involved. In Britain, I have become aware of an enormous range in the content and delivery of this training programme. Some are wholly consultant-led, others organised by specialty registrars themselves. Topics covered away from the "coal face", likewise cover a wide range from plugging the gaps in the curriculum to using this training more to cover generic topics like law and medicine, communication issues, research methodology, ethics etc. Some embrace the importance of research through MSc programmes.

After the first two years, the next three, in terms of specific training programmes, become more the domain of the specialist groups, along with further generic training as outlined by the postgraduate deans. However, while recognising that most passing through Calman training will become paediatricians in district general hospitals (DGHs) with special interests, we have also to accept the need to educate and train tertiary specialists including those who wish an academic training. Those keen to develop their attributes in research and teaching, to introduce innovative methods of training, have also to be accommodated in the complex training programme of the Calman trainee. These situations will continue to pose major challenges.

Little additional money has been made available to provide for all these educational changes demanded, and, indeed, expected of us. The onus, once again, is particularly on consultants who, in general, participate actively in these training programmes as well as in other innovations in service, management, audit and clinical effectiveness and undergraduate teaching. It is also alarming to ponder how so much postgraduate training has relied, and continues to rely, on sponsorship from outside organisations including, dare I say it, milk companies. Take away sponsorship (and a reality of the contemporary scene is that some previous sponsors are becoming lukewarm with loss of the "knock for knock" relationship that has served us all so well) and you also take away many postgraduate training opportunities. This is especially pertinent to the situation in many developing countries where study leave funding for training activities is often non-existent. How has it come about that we have become so reliant on sponsorship for key postgraduate training activities? It has to be recognised that if good training is required this cannot be done on a shoestring and commercial sponsorship. Somehow more money must be made available through trusts and postgraduate deaneries. And, of course, on training days specialist registrars must be available. But who covers the work when they are gone? Consultants once again – who have to teach at the same time!

Recruitment

Just as (conveniently) we may tend not to be that aware how we select students for admission to medical school, so also we do not spend enough time on how to attract the most appropriate people into our own specialty. Who are attracted to paediatrics? When are choices being made? What influences choice? In all this, we have to remind ourselves that paediatrics is not a specialty. It is a very broad church, embracing the subtleties of genetic innovations through to the ravages of poverty on children. Does our discipline appeal to certain types? My experience, after many years of teaching medical students, is that so often medical students who excel in paediatrics at undergraduate level do well in other subjects and are often those who do not appear later. What does this mean? Is paediatrics viewed by some as being too difficult, too boring, too hard? Recruitment is vital and more work is needed to optimise the process. Developing more pre-registration opportunities to help attract people would not come amiss.

We must not forget either the recruitment of paediatricians who are especially driven by academic elements of research and teaching. The future development of paediatrics will rely heavily on those in leading academic posts in partnership with service specialists. Focusing training for service needs at the exclusion of working hard to attract those with an interest in academic aspects is also to live in a fool's paradise. In this context, it is worthwhile recording the words of Jonathan Miller when he contemplated medicine as an undergraduate: "I wasn't driven into medicine by a social conscience but by rampant curiosity."

Conclusions

In this article I have touched on only some aspects of medical education and training that are of special interest to me and in which I was involved when Chairman of the Academic Board in 1994–1997. I hope what I have shown is the enormous activity and commitment by so many dedicated people in Britain to come to terms with this cultural revolution. What we used to learn through serendipity, we now expect and hope will be acquired more through better structured learning. Things were not always easy in the past and we must explore new opportunities for trainees – recognising the revolution in information technology that has magically changed the whole learning process, introducing methods of learning that were simply not possible even a few years ago. As someone especially involved in the undergraduate years, I am optimistic that the new methods of learning, which have their seeds in the medical school years, will carry through into the postgraduate arena. Doctors in the future will rely less on spoonfeeding and will direct their own learning. By being computer literate they will take advantage of the plethora of methods to assist this. But, on a note of caution, I hope not at the expense of gaining clinical expertise. We have to remember that the practice of clinical paediatrics is still an apprenticeship. So much can and must be learned at the bedside and in the clinic. The fact that we learn as we practice is a privilege denied to most professions. It is this, I believe, that is the core that must run through all changes.

A few weeks ago I was at a graduation ceremony for medical students. They were bedecked in cap and gown and graduating with high ideals, reciting in a solemn gorsedd-like chorus the Hippocratic oath in Welsh and English. Their parents were proud and moist-eyed at seeing their offspring receiving their accolades. It is important that we do not let them down. They are our obligation. They, after all, hold the future of medicine in their hands. This is why we must make this cultural revolution work. If it does not, then those whom we have the privilege to serve, our young patients, will be the ones to suffer.

Archives of Disease in Childhood
Bernard Valman

In 1926, two years before the British Paediatric Association (BPA) was founded, the first edition of the *Archives of Disease in Childhood* was published by the British Medical Association (BMA) under the joint editorship of Hugh Thursfield and Reginald Miller. In the introduction to the first edition Thomas Barlow, who was the first to describe infantile scurvy, wrote

> there ought to be an opportunity for key workers in the many departments of children's diseases to publish and submit for criticism and verification their varied observations and experiments; and there is a need to set forth in concrete and detailed form the results of new discoveries in diagnosis and treatment with a view to their employment in practice for the public good.

In the early years of this quarterly journal there were long descriptions of diseases with extensive details of postmortem examination. Papers were often 20 pages in length and contained tedious detail in small print that few readers would tolerate today.

In 1944 two major developments occurred. *The British Journal of Children's Diseases* which had been published for 40 years, had dwindled in size, quality and popularity. The BMA purchased the journal which was effectively incorporated into the *Archives*. The influence of the BPA was assured when it was agreed that the Association would nominate the editors and editorial committee but the nominations would be authorised by the BMA.

The following year, reflecting the fact that editorial policy and direction were provided by the BPA, the name of the Association appeared for the first time on the front cover of the journal which now bore the title *Archives of Disease in Childhood; the Journal of the British Paediatric Association*. The popularity of the *Archives* led to its bimonthly publication from 1951, and in 1973 it was established as a monthly journal.

In 1977, following a suggestion by Donald Court, a joint management committee was formed, and the BMA and BPA became equal business partners and shared the profits accrued by the *Archives*. A new contract was drawn up in 1983 that coincided with a marked fall in the exchange rate for the pound against the dollar. Against this background an expanding overseas market for the journal considerably improved the income to the BPA and the BMA. The financial aspects of the journal remain the responsibility of the management committee, which is composed of the two editors, two representatives of the Royal College of Paediatrics and Child Health and four representatives of the BMA.

In recognition of the wide range of specialist material submitted to the journal, the editors appointed an associate editor in neonatal medicine in 1985. There are now four associate editors advising in different specialties. Since 1990 the *Archives* has benefited from a statistical adviser, and in 1994 a commissioning editor was appointed, in response to the readers" demand for high quality review articles. The review articles, which are each peer reviewed, aim to keep readers up-to-date with advances over the whole field of paediatrics and child health. The Editorial Committee, comprising the above staff and invited members, meets once a year and determines the journal's policy.

The huge expansion in research and practice in perinatal medicine was reflected in the number of high quality papers submitted to the journal, and in 1988 this culminated in the quarterly publication of the *Fetal and Neonatal Edition*, which since 1993 has been published bimonthly.

The *Archives* is considered the foremost of paediatric journals in Europe, and in 1997, based on its impact factor, it was ranked fourth in the world among the non-specialist paediatric journals. The majority of readers are paediatricians actively involved in the provision of child health and paediatric services. In 1998, the journal's circulation was 7920 with 40% of the copies distributed abroad, mainly to Western Europe, USA, Australasia and Japan.

About 1000 original articles are submitted each year and, following peer review and editorial consideration, 25% to 30% are accepted for publication. Of the published papers, 40% are submitted from authors outside the UK. About 100 review articles are published each year.

Since the mid-1980s the numbers of pages have increased from 1000 in the quarto size to 1600 in A4 format. However, scientific journalism has now entered the age of electronic publication, and March 1999 saw the launch of eADC, a full text web site for the standard and Fetal and Neonatal editions of the journal, which offers many attractions including access to MEDLINE and a collected resource facility.

Significant papers

The following papers have been selected and summarised from the *Archives* to show the variety of authors, changing medical practice, or the first or best description of a new finding.

1928

Anaemia in infancy due to iron deficiency has a high prevalence.
MacKay HMM.

1933

First description of Kwashiorkor.
Williams C.

1939

Early reports of the effects of sulphonamides.
Gaisford WF, Morris N, Moncrieff A, and Fleming GB.

1950

Rubella seems able to attack optic lens and cardiovascular system during embryogenesis.
St Huggett A.

1952

Retrolental fibroplasia found in 56 babies in a special care unit during the years 1947–51, suspicion falling on the adverse effect of sudden fluctuations of available oxygen.
Jefferson E.

1963

Homocystinuria: a new inborn error of metabolism.
Carson NAJ, Cusworth DC, Dent CE, Field CMB, Neill DW, and Westall RG.

1966

First comprehensive British growth charts, which were subsequently used throughout the world for growth and development records.
Tanner JM, Whitehouse RH, and Takaishi M.

1967

Sugar malabsorption due to deficiencies of disaccharidase activities and of monosaccharide transport.
Holzel A.

First description of methylmalonic aciduria causing metabolic acidosis.
Oberholzer VG, Levin B, Burgess EA, and Young WF.

1970

A thermal neutral environment reduces oxygen consumption and evaporative water loss to a minimum.
Hey EM, and Katz G.

1971

Effect of human growth hormone treatment for 1–7 years on growth of a hundred children.
Tanner JM, Whitehouse RH, Hughes PCR, and Vince FP.

1972

Renal transplantation in 19 children.
Hulme B, Kenyon JR, Owen K, Snell M, Mowbray JF, Porter KA, Starkie SJ, Muras H, and Peart WS.

1973

Changes in ventilator management reduced mortality from hyaline membrane disease and incidence of bronchopulmonary dysplasia.
Herman S, and Reynolds EOR.

1974

Good correlation between arterial and transcutaneous oxygen levels in the newborn.
Huch R, Lubbers DW, and Hutch A.

1976

Fifteen year developmental study on the effects of severe undernutrition during infancy on subsequent physical growth and intellectual functioning.
Stoch MB, and Smythe PM.

Diabetic ketosis treated by adding low dose insulin to rehydrating fluid.
Malleson PN.

1978

Computed axial tomography and acute neurological problems of childhood.
Day RE, Thompson JLG, and Schutt WH.

Viral infection as a precipitant of wheeze in children; combined home and hospital study.
Mitchell I, Inglish JM, and Simpson H.

1982

Munchausen syndrome by proxy.
Meadow SR.

1983

Nuclear magnetic resonance imaging of the brain.
Bydder GM, and Whitelaw A.

1984

Clinical use of DNA markers linked to the gene for Duchenne muscular dystrophy.
Pembrey ME, Davies KE, Winter RM, Elles RG, Williamson R, Fazzone TA, and Walker C.

1985

Virulence genes in prevention of *Haemophilus influenzae* infections.
Moxon ER.

First paper in UK suggesting an association between factor VIII usage and AIDS in children with haemophilia.
Beddall AC, Al-Rubei K, Williams MD, and Hill FGH.

1989

Safety and immunogenicity of a *Haemophilus influenzae* vaccine shown in Oxford region.
Tudor-Williams G, Frankland J, Isaacs D, Mayon-White RT, Macfarlane JA, Rees DG, and Moxon ER.

Prospective study of vertical transmission of HIV.
Mok RA, Hague PL, Yap PL, Hargreaves FD et al.

1997

Bone marrow transplantation for mucopolysaccharidosis type I.
Vellodi A, Young EP, Cooper A, Wraith JE et al.

1998

Treatment of hypoxic–ischaemic brain damage by moderate hypothermia.
Edwards AD, Wyatt JS, and Thosen M.

1998 contd

What's to be done about the malaise in science training in paediatrics and child health.
Aynsley-Green A.

Systematic review of the school entry medical examination.
Barlow J, Stewart-Brown S, and Fletcher J.

Increased survival and deteriorating developmental outcome in 23 to 25 week old gestation infants, 1990–4 compared with 1984–9.
Emsley HCA, Wardle SP, Sims DG, Chiswick ML, and D'Souza SW.

Transition from school to adult life for physically disabled young people.
Fiorentino L, Datta D, Gentle S, Hall DMB et al.

1999

Continuous neonatal blood gas monitoring using a multiparameter intra-arterial sensor.
Morgan C, Newell SJ, Ducker DA, Hodgkinson J et al.

Unnatural sudden infant death.
Meadow R.

Meta-analysis of elective high frequency ventilation.
Cools F, and Offrinea M.

Telemedicine in paediatric cardiology.
Casey FA.

Distinguishing between "no evidence of effect" and "evidence of no effect" in randomised controlled trials.
Tarnow-Mordi WO, and Healy MJR.

Growth of long-term survivors of liver transplantation.
Viner RM, Forton JTM, Cole TJ, Clark IH, Noble-Jamieson G, and Barnes ND.

The paucity of cited papers between 1989 and 1997 may be due to the perception of the historical significance of published papers at the present point in time. The novelty of recent papers gives them a temporary advantage.

Winning the battle for a College
Roy Meadow

The history *The British Paediatric Association 1928–1988* reveals how the topic of College status became an increasingly important subject of discussion and debate for paediatricians. During the 1970s and 1980s the subject dominated the business at annual general meetings, and led to important referenda of BPA members. The 1987 referendum had shown almost equal support for a Faculty of Paediatrics within the Royal Colleges of Physicians of the UK, and an independent College. The outgoing President, John Forfar, and his successor June Lloyd, were members of a sub-committee established to consider the result of that referendum. It proposed to Council that steps should be taken to establish a College of Paediatricians *interdependent* with the three Royal Colleges of Physicians. With Council's support, the motion was overwhelmingly accepted at the 1988 AGM in York. But much depended upon the interpretation of "interdependent". Difficult negotiations commenced with the London, Edinburgh and Glasgow Colleges. The outcome was a series of proposals which were put to BPA members in 1990, and which culminated in a referendum on the question "should the British Paediatric Association proceed to establish closer integration with the Royal Colleges of Physicians of the UK, as outlined in the attached proposals, but continue to maintain its independence to speak on behalf of paediatrics and child health?" In the subsequent ballot 469 (38.5%) voted "yes", and 745 (61.5%) voted "no". Thus, proposals to integrate the BPA more closely with the RCPs were doomed. The corollary was that those who favoured an independent College believed that the wind of change was strengthening, and that the many new colleagues in the rapidly expanding specialty of paediatrics felt less allegiance to the RCPs than did their predecessors.

More than half of the BPA's 2400 members had joined in the previous 10 years, and their training and life had changed dramatically in that time. Unlike their teachers, trainees were entering paediatrics immediately after registration. In the past most paediatricians had had to work in adult medicine in order to pass the adult MRCP, but the creation of a Paediatric MRCP Clinical Examination altered that. Moreover, it was clear that European law was going to demand a more structured and shorter specialist training, which would entail total immersion in paediatrics.

June Lloyd, the President, though personally committed to an independent College, had represented the divergence of views within the Association with great integrity, and had conducted the negotiations with the three RCPs with care and firmness. The 1990 vote, however, was a signal that paediatricians might be prepared to commit themselves to change. The incoming President was David Hull. He had been elected unopposed and commanded great respect. In the past he had been a listener rather than a mover in the debates about College status. However, in his first year of presidency, he quickly demonstrated his commitment to change by leading Council to seek a further referendum of members, in March 1992, to answer the question "Do you wish the British Paediatric Association to proceed to apply for a Charter to become a College?" Of 1267 ballot papers returned, 62% were in favour, 38% were against. Some of those disagreeing with the outcome pointed out that 700 members had not taken up the opportunity to vote and, therefore, there was not a clear majority in favour of College status. Most members, though, accepted that the referendum result was a mandate for change, and Council and its officers were clear in that view. Following a unanimous vote of BPA Council in June 1992, the Honorary Officers were instructed to proceed to seek a Charter to become a College.

Negotiations with the Privy Council

Detailed planning began. To become a College the BPA had to lodge its application with the Privy Council. Mr Bertie Leigh, of Hempsons Solicitors, was engaged to draft the Petition, Bye-Laws and Charter. Preliminary meetings were held between senior officers of the Privy Council and senior BPA officers. The meetings took place in the Cabinet Office at the corner of Downing Street and Whitehall. Those of us participating were met with courtesy (and cups of tea). The main impression from the meetings with the Privy Council officers was of their caution, their reluctance to consider change, their respect for the ancient Colleges, and their wish not to upset the *status quo*. At one of the early meetings, the Clerk to the Privy Council asked if the BPA had considered the possibility of becoming a Faculty of the RCP! Despite the negative vibrations, the BPA officers and Secretariat worked with Hempsons to produce the draft Petition, Bye-Laws and Charter. These were approved by BPA Council before being lodged formally with the Privy Council in February 1994. The draft Petition required a resolution to be put to our Annual General Meeting. At the April 1994 Annual General Meeting in Warwick, the last to be presided over by David Hull, members voted by an overwhelming majority (94%) in favour of empowering the Council of the Association "to take all the necessary steps to petition the Queen's most Excellent Majesty and Council".

In the *London Gazette* of 22nd July 1994 notice was given of the Petition from the BPA, asking that all Petitions for or against the granting of a Royal Charter should be delivered to the Privy Council before 13th September 1994.

During the final six months of his presidency, David Hull had taken time off from his department in Nottingham to work with the Secretariat to produce the documentation to win the political argument. An important document *The work of the British Paediatric Association 1994*, was a 16 page booklet illustrating the range of activities of the BPA, which gave the reasons why College status was appropriate - because:

- The medical care of children is a discipline distinct from medical care of adults
- The nation needs a body that speaks for the health needs of, and health services for, its children
- The health service needs a body to promote the practice of paediatric medicine, and to encourage doctors to train as paediatricians.

The contest to succeed David Hull as President involved five candidates, and it was the one most closely identified with the campaign for College status, Roy Meadow, who won. He had proposed (and lost) the motion that the BPA should become a College, at the AGM in Lancaster in 1973 and now, more than 20 years later, had the opportunity to make it happen.

The opposition continues

The Privy Council had made clear that we had an uphill task, and that we needed the support of other Colleges and of influential people in the medical establishment.

There were three outstanding difficulties that kept arising during the negotiations with the Privy Council and the Department of Health:

1. That the BPA did not (and perhaps could not) fulfil all the duties of a Medical Royal College. This was true, partly because BPA members usually were doing that work on behalf of one of the RCPs. Moreover, the BPA could not be responsible for medical examinations until it was a College, and had the right to run such examinations. However, steps were taken, often to the annoyance of the London RCP, to ensure that the BPA controlled and ran as many of the tasks of a College as possible. A Continuing Medical Education (CME) programme was established by the Academic Board; the foundations of a Joint Paediatric Training Committee were established from the Specialist Advisory Committee in Paediatrics; regular separate meetings of Regional Advisers in Paediatrics were set up; District Paediatric Tutors were appointed; a full consultation and nomination process was established for the recommendation of Merit Awards; the Health Services, Manpower and Research Divisions were expanded. Thus, the BPA was able to say that it was fulfilling College tasks for paediatrics and child health as fully, and rather better than the three RCPs, and could do so more effectively because it represented the whole UK.
2. A second problem was that a substantial, and influential, minority of members did not wish the BPA to become an independent College. However the size of that minority declined dramatically about the time of the public quarrels with the London RCP in early 1995, which are described later. When under attack, members unite and forget their differences.
3. The third obstacle was that other Colleges and influential medical organisations did not appear to support our Petition.

Ammunition was needed. Support was required from other medical organisations, and there had to be no opposition from the Department of Health, or any part of government.

Rallying support

A letter setting out our aims, together with *The work of the British Paediatric Association 1994*, and a summary of the case for a College, was sent to the Presidents of all Medical Royal Colleges, and the major medical organisations, with a request for a letter of written support which could be forwarded to the Privy Council. Suitable letters of reply were few. Long-standing friends and supporters, such as the RCGP and the RCOG, sent cogent letters of support. Some other Colleges with which paediatricians had thought they had good working relationships were not able to provide letters of support. Their President usually telephoned or wrote a personal letter to say how sorry they were that despite their personal sympathy for the cause, their Council would not endorse a letter of support for a Paediatric College. Successive BPA Presidents had kept the Presidents of the RCPs closely informed about what was happening. On taking office in 1994, the new President sought to gain the support of Professor Turnberg, President of the RCP London. Support was not forthcoming. However, the support of the two Scottish Colleges (RCP Edinburgh and RCPS Glasgow) was an important factor at a time when so many of the ancient Colleges were very nervous of another new College diminishing their own prestige, power and income. The case was presented at the Conference (Academy) of Medical Royal Colleges – the meeting of all College Presidents. Several seemed to fear that a Paediatric College would seek to attract members from them (e.g. paediatric surgeons, child psychiatrists, intensivists). The then Chairman (Turnberg) was in a strong position and advised the meeting not to endorse the proposal.

The President sent out a further series of letters, together with full documentation, to paediatric organisations abroad, and to over a hundred professional organisations and charities concerned with children, seeking their written support, for delivery to the Privy Council. The response was overwhelming, it was clear that most of those organisations had the greatest respect for the BPA, valued its work and supported change that would enhance that work. Paediatric organisations in Europe and beyond pointed out how the UK was out of line with most of the world in failing to recognise paediatrics as a major specialty.

In the continuing discussions with the Privy Council, it became clear that the lack of support from the London RCP was a major obstacle. Other specialties had achieved College status after an interim period as a Faculty of a parent College, and usually with the support of that College. The Privy Council seemed to view the BPA as a rebel group within the RCP. Letters of support for our Petition were numerous, but the Privy Council seemed to pay great attention to the letters of opposition, whether they be from a few former officers of the BPA, or from the ancient and influential Colleges. Even the Department of Health seemed nervous of the ancient Colleges.

Opposition unites members of the BPA

Paradoxically, the opposition of the RCP became helpful. In the winter of 1994 the RCP President formally responded to the Privy Council opposing the Petition. This letter infuriated many paediatricians who, themselves, were Fellows of the RCP, because it seemed that the President was expressing the RCP view, without consulting its governing body comitia, or its elected Council (where the issue had not been discussed).

More than 1400 people attended the BPA Meeting in York in 1995. There was a very large attendance for the AGM, and much anger and concern expressed then, and subsequently, concerning the RCP's response to our petition. Some of the more vociferous members suggested that paediatricians should resign from the RCP, or take other retaliatory action. The opposition of the RCP, and the way in which it had been presented to the Privy Council, had united BPA members in support of the proposed College to an extent that seemed unlikely six months earlier. Members made it plain that they wished Council and its President to press our case to become a College urgently. By now the BPA had 3300 members, a third of whom were consultants; the demand for College status was strong.

The strength of feeling within the BPA became known to the RCP where, in June 1995, its Council discussed, for the first time since the submission to the Privy Council, the issue of an independent College of Paediatrics. Each of the five paediatric representatives, including the

---

Sir,

Royal College of Paediatricians?

I write to protest against the proposed formation of a Royal College of Paediatricians. It is quite unnecessary. Paediatrics is an important branch of medicine, but so are cardiology, chest medicine, gastroenterology, neurology, nephrology, hepatology, haematology, endocrinology, dermatology, etc. All branches are equally important to the general body of medicine. Each new college diminishes the prestige and power of the existing colleges. When is it going to stop? If the present trend continues, the next thing will be a college for every disease. I look forward, sadly, to Royal Colleges of Flat Feet and Halitosis.

ALEXANDER COOKE
Retired Physician

Letter to the editor of the *Journal of the Royal College of Physicians of London*

Paediatric Vice President and Censor, explained why they now believed it necessary for there to be a separate College of Paediatrics (two of them explaining that in the past they had not held that view). The paediatricians emphasised that they intended to work closely with physicians, and that the formation of a College should lead to improvement in relationships, rather than reverse. As was usual at RCP Council, no vote was taken. After the Council meeting, the President of the London College wrote suggesting a new working party between the BPA and the College to explore "new initiatives, such as formation of a Faculty". BPA Council, meeting a few weeks later, had no enthusiasm for yet another working group. It was fully aware of the considerable efforts that had been made in the past to create a Faculty, and its rejection by the BPA membership. Paediatrics was a mainstream specialty, both in undergraduate and in postgraduate training, and should be represented by a College.

The Regional Advisers who acted for both the BPA and the Colleges of Physicians, and many of whom had great loyalty to the ancient Colleges, nevertheless recognised the changes that had taken place in the structure of paediatric training, and the need for paediatrics to be represented, as of right, on the Academy of Colleges. They expressed their unanimous support for a formal letter from them to the Privy Council in support of the Petition. It was a persuasive letter, signed by many senior paediatricians who had the closest links with the three RCPs, many of whom were, or had been, office holders or Council members of the three RCPs.

The Department of Health had a key role in advising the Privy Council. Several private meetings were held with the Chief Medical Officer (CMO), Dr Kenneth Calman, and others in the Department. The CMO was identified with the creation of shorter structured medical training (Calman Training), and involved in the complicated legislation to oversee it and the creation of the Specialist Training Authority (STA). It was unthinkable that paediatrics would not be represented on the STA, and yet the rules proposed that only Colleges should be represented, not Associations of specialists. Our response was that the BPA should become a College, and thereby become a full member of both the Academy of Colleges and the Specialist Training Authority. The CMO was a sympathetic listener ("in listening mode" as he called it), but made no promises. The DoH informed me that its papers would be placed before the relevant Ministers at the end of the summer, and that the Privy Council would then be advised.

The impression was that not only Dr Calman, but also other members of the Department of Health, had great respect for the work of the BPA, and had no doubt that in relation to matters of child health the BPA was the appropriate organisation with which to deal, thus acknowledging that in many ways the BPA already fulfilled the role of a medical Royal College. On the other hand, the Department was involved in difficult negotiations within the European Union in relation to the creation of the Specialist Training Authority. In this work they were assisted, and to some extent led, by Sir Leslie Turnberg, the current Chairman of College Presidents. There was an understandable reluctance to overrule him on the Paediatric College when he was such a far sighted, wise and effective leader on the European issue.

Successful conclusion

Lobbying at Westminster, at medical meetings, in journals and with professional colleagues at home and abroad continued. There was genuine uncertainty about the outcome and considerable foreboding. Then, in January 1996, a letter was received from the Clerk to the Privy Council:

> The Privy Council, having considered the Petition, are minded, without prejudice to recommend to Her Majesty that a Charter be granted.

The news arrived during a meeting of the Academic Board. Champagne replaced orange juice at lunchtime. There followed a busy period in which the Charter and Bye-Laws for our new College were refined and approved by Council.

Perhaps the last major argument concerned the title. Those of us who favoured a new College had, from the beginning, believed that it should be more than a union or society of paediatricians, but also an organisation that promoted the health needs of children. Traditionalists wanted a "College of *Paediatricians*" which would have been in line with every other medical Royal College, making clear that it was a College of specialists. However, Council agreed that we would seek a "College of *Paediatrics and Child Health*", and that we would seek the approval of that title from our members at the AGM. As expected the debate was vigorous, but there was an overwhelming vote in favour of the longer, and more holistic, title. The battle was not quite over. Several other Colleges, presumably mindful of the potentially high profile of a College of Paediatrics and Child Health, objected to the title, but at the meeting of College Presidents it was easy to point out that it was the business of paediatricians, and not other specialists, to decide what their College was called, and that paediatricians would not suggest alterations to the title of Colleges other than their own. The move for the Academy of Colleges to intervene with the Privy Council was resisted. The College of Paediatrics and Child Health received its Charter on 23rd August 1996.

The appellation "Royal" comes on the recommendation of a Department within the Home Office, and is separate from the granting of a Royal Charter. Our initial Charter was for a College of Paediatrics and Child Health. Previously, we had submitted papers to the Home Office requesting that it would be appropriate for us to be a "Royal" College from the beginning, rather than to be on probation for several years before achieving the Royal appellation, as has happened to other medical Colleges. The argument was accepted, but administrative problems within Government caused a delay of two months, until October 17th 1996, before we were entitled to use the present full title. Almost as if to confirm that final maturity, Her Royal Highness the Princess Royal graciously agreed to become our first Patron.

Chapter 5: Looking forward

College strategy
PA Hamilton

Our pride in making the transition from an Association to a Royal College has been accompanied by the challenge of taking forward our aspirations for a better children's health service. We deliberately named our College after our specialty rather than our specialists and we need a strategy that can justify this name. During the time that we were the BPA many committees were already working on training, quality and research issues. There was concern however that the College might confuse activity with achievement and lack of overall direction. It is possible for all the engine rooms of a ship to be working perfectly but the ship itself to be going round in circles.

We therefore decided to draw up a strategy that would be a five year plan for the College. It is called "A Strategy for a Children's Health Service" and is designed to have aspirations that are achievable and prioritised so that energies can be directed appropriately. It was decided that each year an annual implementation plan will document the aims that have been achieved and those prioritised for the next year.

The views of Chairs of the committees were canvassed and a draft strategy was presented at the first Conference of Committees in February 1998. At the conference the Strategy was debated and re-drafted. The final draft was approved by Council and discussed at the spring meeting. The seven points of the final Strategy have since provided the focus for the College's on-going activities.

In late 1998 the Chairs of all the committees drew up work plans for 1999 to form the basis of the first annual implementation plan. From these work plans, a draft implementation plan was presented at the Conference of Committees in February 1999. It was gratifying to find that already many of the action points had been achieved and others had formed the focus of an aim for the coming year.

The first strategy point is entitled **Education, Vocation and Workforce**. Its aims are to ensure that the highest quality of education for trainees is provided and that they are given information on career choices in paediatrics. The College also aims to stimulate a sense of vocation in trainees. We need to recruit and retain appropriate numbers of specialist paediatricians and to ensure that the future need for consultants is adequately met. In working towards this aim the College has appointed officers for workforce, examinations and continuing professional development. The General Professional Training Committee has published *Essential Features for SHO Posts* and *Certificates of Satisfactory Training for SHOs*. It is working with the RCGP to develop "stem cell posts" suitable for trainees planning careers in either general practice or in paediatrics. The Higher Specialist Training Committee is developing more formal appraisal and assessment portfolios for Specialist Registrars. The officer for workforce has the challenging task of predicting future numbers of consultants and trainees.

The second strategy point relates to **Quality and Standards**. The aim is to define and sustain the highest standards of paediatric practice and to assess quality of performance. The quality of practice committee and the research unit will work to promote clinical effectiveness through development and implementation of evidence-based medicine. The Clinical Governance Board will coordinate mechanisms for clinical governance in relation to the performance of individual practitioners and of clinical services. The College will publish "Duties of a Paediatrician" and define what it means to be a Member or Fellow "in good standing". The Specialty Board will work towards setting service specifications and the General Professional Training Committee is looking at linking service accreditation to training visits.

Scholarship, Research and Information form the basis of the third strategy point. The College wishes to promote an academic approach to paediatrics and to highlight the importance of research. It will support university departments of paediatrics and clinical academic trainees. The Research Unit will work to assess and grade data through a systematic review of the scientific literature and to provide information, evidence and advice on aspects of the health care of children and young people. The Academic Panel plans to compile a map of academic paediatrics and a database of academic paediatricians to help trainees wishing to pursue academic careers. The College will commission an annual report on the health of the nation's children and publish guidelines on the ethics of research in children.

A major task facing the College is the future **Configuration of Services** and this is the fourth strategy point. The aim is to configure a high quality, coordinated, child-centred health service which best serves the needs of the child and family. There are currently joint working parties between our College and other relevant Colleges looking at the configuration of adolescent services, community child health services and maternity services. There are plans to hold a seminar on the future Configuration of Services in autumn 1999. The challenge is to achieve the best use of resources in joint planning and funding between health, social and educational services while highlighting the special needs of children and their families.

Advocacy and Equality issues are covered by the fifth point. We aim to be advocates for the rights of children and young people in society and to promote their health needs and services. The advocacy committee is lobbying for national recognition of the effects of poverty on children's health. The patient liaison committee hopes, in association with other bodies, to integrate the opinions of children, parents and their representatives in improving child health services. The Committee plans to publish a document for members on how to be advocates for children.

The College recognises its responsibility to **International Child Health**. The sixth strategy point outlines its desire to forge links with others working in international paediatrics and health care. A database of members willing to give service internationally has been set up and the first International Task Force Conference has been a success.

Finally the strategy deals with the **Structure and Function** of the College itself. The aim is to promote a dynamic College, governed by Council and representing the membership. A document outlining the Structure and Function has been published and circulated. The report on ethical commercial sponsorship is being completed. Regional Committees are being set up to strengthen the representation of the College locally and the web site is now open.

We hope the Strategy and the annual Implementation Plans will ensure our College achieves the goals its members and the public expect of it.

Structure of the College
KL Dodd

The main objectives of the College are:

- to advance the art and science of paediatrics
- improving standards of medical care to children
- to educate and examine doctors in paediatrics.

Responsibilities

Medical Royal Colleges have direct responsibility for postgraduate and medical education, continuing professional development and setting and, in future, monitoring standards of medical practice. In the Royal College of Paediatrics and Child Health these responsibilities include:

- setting syllabuses and paediatric training
- approving posts for doctors training
- MRCPCH and DCH examinations
- recommending to the Specialist Training Authority the award of a Certificate of Completion of Specialist Training (CCST)
- providing College assessors to all consultant paediatrician appointment interviews in England and Wales (via national panels in Scotland).

In addition there are many matters on which the College may seek to have influence including:

- content of undergraduate medical education
- medical staffing and workforce
- configuration of child health services
- clinical and health service research
- advice to Government and other bodies
- health service funding and priorities
- advocacy for children and their carers
- international child health.

Governance

The College has a formal constitution. Changes to the Charter and Bye-Laws must have the approval of the Privy Council and Charity Commissioners as well as the College's Annual General Meeting.

Council is the governing body of the College and comprises the elected regional representatives and honorary officers, a limited number of ex officio members (who together serve as the Trustees of the College) and observers. As it meets only three times a year it devolves responsibility to other committees such as the Finance Committee and Executive Committee.

Matters of major policy are determined by Council while other discussions are brought to Council for ratification.

The College structure

The College structure is shown in the organisation chart. The Executive Committee comprises elected honorary officers, senior officers who are elected by national ballot, and others elected by Council. It maintains a watching brief on all committee activities and presents matters for debate, decision or ratification to Council.

The President's Advisory Group meets regularly to assist liaison between the President and Senior Officers.

Each major area of work is led by a Senior Officer and the portfolios of the two Vice Presidents are not fixed.

Other College officers, elected by Council, carry specific responsibility for areas of work such as cardiologist training, general professional training and continuing professional development.

Groups such as the Regional Advisers, Specialty Board, and Science Advisory Committee have responsibility spanning the divisional structure of the College. Others, including Advocacy, Ethics, the International Board and the College Appeal are responsible to Council via the Executive Committee.

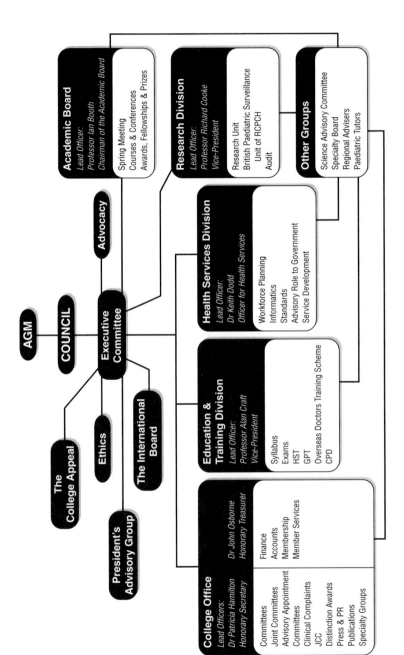

Structure of the Royal College of Paediatrics and Child Health

AGM

COUNCIL

Executive Committee

The College Appeal

Ethics

President's Advisory Group

The International Board

Advocacy

Academic Board
Lead Officer:
Professor Ian Booth
Chairman of the Academic Board

Spring Meeting
Courses & Conferences
Awards, Fellowships & Prizes

Research Division
Lead Officer:
Professor Richard Cooke
Vice-President

Research Unit
British Paediatric Surveillance Unit of RCPCH
Audit

Other Groups

Science Advisory Committee
Specialty Board
Regional Advisers
Paediatric Tutors

Health Services Division
Lead Officer:
Dr Keith Dodd
Officer for Health Services

Workforce Planning
Informatics
Standards
Advisory Role to Government
Service Development

Education & Training Division
Lead Officer:
Professor Alan Craft
Vice-President

Syllabus
Exams
HST
GPT
Overseas Doctors Training Scheme
CPD

College Office
Lead Officers:
Dr Patricia Hamilton
Honorary Secretary

Dr John Osborne
Honorary Treasurer

Committees
Joint Committees
Advisory Appointment Committees
Clinical Complaints
JCC
Distinction Awards
Press & PR
Publications
Specialty Groups

Finance
Accounts
Membership
Member Services

Standing committees

These include:

- the Ethics Advisory Committee
- Advocacy Committee
- Medicines Committee
- International Board
- Community Child Health Services
- Trainees
- Clinical Directors
- Child Protection
- Disability
- Immunisation and Infectious Disease
- Nutrition.

There are separate Scottish and Welsh committees (the establishment of an Irish committee is under consideration) and a regional committee structure is being developed in England.

Joint standing committees

These serve to effect liaison, usually at Senior Officer level, between the College and other bodies including RCGP, RCOG, RCN, RCPath and many others.

Representation on outside bodies

The College is represented on a number of major government committees and national organisations including the Academy of Medical Royal Colleges, Specialist Training Authority, General Medical Council, Standing Medical Advisory Committee, the JCC and others.

It also has links with international organisations including the Confederation of European Societies of Paediatrics, the International Paediatric Association and the World Health Organisation.

Working parties and publications

The College has a long-standing and successful record in convening working groups to produce reports on specific topics or problems. Some of the larger working parties are intercollegiate with membership from a wide range of medical and other professional disciplines, including charities concerned with children's welfare.

The present divisional structure of the College has been developed to meet our present needs but will inevitably need to change in response to new commitments, including for example postgraduate examinations and clinical governance.

Chapter 6: Royal College of Paediatrics and Child Health

Officers of the College

Professor Richard Cooke
Acting President

Professor Ian Booth
Chairman of the Academic Board

Professor David Hall
President Elect

Professor Richard Cooke
Vice President (Research)

Professor Alan Craft
Vice President (Academic)

Professor John Osborne
Honorary Treasurer

Dr Patricia Hamilton
Honorary Secretary

Dr Andrew Long
Assistant to the Honorary Secretary

Dr Janet Anderson
Donald Court Fellow: General Professional Training

Dr Martin Brueton
Higher Specialist Training

Dr Keith Dodd
Health Services

Dr Nick Mann
Honorary Editor

Dr Sheila Shribman
Workforce Planning

Professor Michael Weindling
Continuing Professional Development

Dr Tom Turner
Scotland

Dr John Morgan
Wales

Past Officers

Presidents

Prof George Frederic Still		Prof F M B Allen	1955–56
(Sir Frederic Still)	1928	Prof J O Craig	1956–57
Dr Edmund Cautley	1928–29	Dr K H Tallerman	1957–58
Dr H Morley Fletcher	1929–30	Dr J Forest Smith	1958–59
Dr Robert Hutchison		Dr R C Lightwood	1959–60
(Sir Robert Hutchison bt)	1930–31	Prof A V Neale	1960–61
Dr F John Poynton	1931–32	Prof A A Moncrieff	
Dr A Dingwall-Fordyce	1932–33	(Sir Alan Moncrieff)	1961–62

Dr Eric Pritchard	1933–34	Dr C F Harris	
Dr J H Thursfield	1934–35	(Sir Charles Harris)	1962–63
Prof A E Naish	1935–36	Sir Wilfrid Sheldon	1963–64
Dr Leonard Findlay	1936–37	Prof W F Gaisford	1964–65
Dr J Wilkie Scott	1937–38	Emeritus Prof R W B Ellis	1965–66
Dr H C Cameron	1938–39	Prof A G Watkins	1966–67
Prof C M McNeil	1939–42	Prof E R Steen	1967–68
Prof L G Parsons		Dr A White Franklin	1968–69
(Sir Leonard Parsons)	1942–45	Prof J H Hutchison	1969–70
Prof G B Fleming	1945–46	Dr R H Dobbs	1970–71
Prof C W Vining	1946–47	Prof J L Henderson	1971–72
Dr Donald Paterson	1947–48	Prof J D Hay	1972–73
Dr H T Ashby	1948–49	Prof S D M Court	1973–76
Dr A G Maitland-Jones	1949–50	Prof O H Wolff	1976–79
Sir James Spence	1950–51	Dr G M Komrower	1979–82
Prof N B Capon	1951–52	Prof Sir Peter Tizard	1982–85
Prof J M Smellie	1952–53	Prof J O Forfar	1985–88
Dr B E Schlesinger	1953–54	Prof Dame June Lloyd	1988–91
Prof Stanley Graham	1954–55	Prof Sir David Hull	1991–94
		Prof Sir Roy Meadow	1994–97
		Prof J D Baum	1997–99

Vice Presidents

Dr Roderick MacFaul	1994–97	Prof David Hall	1994–98

Honorary Treasurers

Dr H Morley Fletcher	1928–37	Prof Charlotte Anderson	1971–75
Dr Donald Paterson	1937–47	Dr G M Komrower	1975–78
Dr R C Lightwood	1947–58	Dr A D M Jackson	1978–83
		Dr W J Appleyard	1983–88
Prof A G Watkins	1958–64	Dr J W Partridge	1988–91
Prof J D Hay	1964–71	Dr Christopher Nourse	1991–96

Honorary Secretaries

Dr Donald Paterson	1928–34	Dr Donald Paterson and	
Dr A G Maitland-Jones	1934–43	Dr B M Laurance	1971–75
Dr Donald Paterson	1943–45	Prof June Lloyd	1975–79
Prof Alan Moncrieff	1945–54	Dr D R Harvey	1979–84
Dr P R Evans	1954–59	Dr T L Chambers	1984–89
Dr E W Hart	1959–65	Dr Roderick MacFaul	1989–94
Prof T E Oppé	1965–71	Dr Keith Dodd	1994–99

Honorary Officers

Dr W Henderson	1964–72	Dr Keith Dodd	1989–94
Dr A D M Jackson	1973–76	Dr Leon Polnay	1990–94
Dr C H Nourse	1976–81	Dr Graham Clayden	1992–97
Dr M M Liberman	1977–80	Dr Sam Lingam	1994–97
Dr D W Fielding	1980–85	Dr Mary McGraw	1994–97
Dr T L Chambers	1981–84	Dr Margaret Lynch	1995–98
Dr Roderick MacFaul	1985–89	Dr David Milligan	1994–98
Dr Marion Miles	1984–90	Dr Sheila Shribman	1995–98

Chairmen of the Academic Board

Prof D V Hubble	1966–69	Prof A G M Campbell	1981–84
Prof S D M Court	1969–72	Prof David Baum	1984–87
Prof J A Davis	1972–75	Prof R D H Boyd	1987–90
Prof R G Mitchell	1975–78	Prof Roy Meadow	1990–94
Prof D Hull	1978–81	Prof David Davies	1994–97
		Prof Andrew Wilkinson	1997–98

Secretaries to the Academic Board

Prof J A Davis	1966–67	Dr David Baum	1980–84
Dr A D M Jackson	1967–73	Dr R W I Cooke	1984–89
Dr Roy Meadow	1973–76	Prof Janet Eyre	1989–92
Dr R D H Boyd	1976–80	Dr Andrew Wilkinson	1993–97

Honorary Editors

Dr Harvey Marcovitch	1993–97

Awards, Lectures and Fellowships

James Spence Medal

This medal commemorates Sir James Spence (1892-1954) who was Professor of Child Health at the University of Newcastle upon Tyne and one of the principals who founded and developed the British Paediatric Association. The award is supported by a generous endowment given to the BPA (subsequently the Royal College of Paediatrics and Child Health) in 1957 by the James Spence Memorial Committee.

1. The medal is known as the James Spence Medal and is usually presented with a volume of the collected writings of Sir James Spence to the medallist at an Annual Meeting.

2. The award is made from time to time for outstanding contributions to the advancement or clarification of paediatric knowledge.

3. Persons working in the United Kingdom or in any country of the British Commonwealth within the fields of clinical or social paediatrics, clinical science, epidemiology or family practice are usually considered for the award, but neither those working in other countries nor in the other scientific disciplines are necessarily excluded.

4. The award shall be made on the recommendation of the Council of the Royal College of Paediatrics and Child Health after it has been advised by the Executive Committee.

5. In accordance with the wishes of the James Spence Memorial Committee, interest accumulated after payment for casting each medal and for travelling and other expenses arising out of the award shall be used by the Royal College of Paediatrics and Child Health for any other purpose which will foster the advancement of paediatrics.

6. The trustees of the endowment fund shall be the Treasurer and the Honorary Secretary of the Royal College of Paediatrics and Child Health.

1960	Professor A A Moncrieff	1982	Dr D MacCarthy
1961	Professor R A McCance	1983	Professor J O Forfar
1963	Sir Macfarlane Burnet	1984	Dr J W B Douglas
1964	Professor L S Penrose	1985	Dr N S Gordon
1965	Dr Cicely Williams	1986	Sir Peter Tizard
1967	Professor R R A Coombs	1987	Professor J L Emery
1968	Dr Mary Sheridan	1987	Dr F J W Miller
1968	Dr D W Winnicott	1988	Professor O H Wolff
1969	Dr G S Dawes	1989	Professor D C Morley
1970	Professor D V Hubble	1990	Professor L B Strang
1971	Dr W W Payne	1991	Professor J A Davis
1972	Dr R C MacKeith	1992	Emeritus Professor R W Smithells
1973	Professor C A Clarke	1993	Professor Dame June Lloyd
1974	Dr J Bowlby	1994	Professor E O R Reynolds
1976	Dr D Gairdner	1995	Emeritus Professor R H R White
1977	Professor R S Illingworth	1996	Professor Sir David Hull
1978	Professor S D M Court	1997	Dr Barbara Ansell
1979	Professor K W Cross	1998	Professor Forrester Cockburn
1980	Professor J M Tanner	1999	Professor David Harvey
1981	Dr Elsie Widdowson		Sir Roy Meadow

George Frederic Still Memorial Lecture
(Endowed by the late G W Bray)

George Frederic Still (1868-1941) was physician at The Hospital for Sick Children, Great Ormond Street and physician and Professor of Diseases of Children at King's College Hospital. He was President of the International Paediatric Association and first President of the British Paediatric Association.

RULES

1. That the lecture shall be known as the George Frederic Still Memorial lecture.

2. That it shall be given biennially by an eminent physician or scientist, not necessarily a paediatrician, to be selected by the Academic Board.

3. That the honorarium attaching to such lecture be £100.

4. That the expenses of the lecturer incurred at the Annual Meeting shall be borne by the College.

LECTURERS

1943   Prof S P Bedson "Some recent work on virus diseases and its practical import"

1945   Dr R Cruickshank "Infection in infancy"

1947   Dr H Waller "Some clinical aspects of lactation"

1949   Prof A St G McC Huggett "Foetal physiology and child health"

1951   Dr J A Fraser Roberts "Genetics and paediatrics"

1953   Prof A C Frazer "Absorption from the intestine"

1955   Prof F A E Crew "Medicine and social science"

1957   Prof C Dent "Hartnup disease – an inborn error of metabolism"

1959   Dr G S Dawes "Respiratory and cardiovascular problems after birth"

1961   Dr J H Ebbs "Moniliasis"

1963   Dr W M Court Brown "Cytogenetics and paediatrics. A current appraisal and future prospects"

1965   Dr H L Barnett "Paediatric nephrology: the scientific study of the kidneys and their diseases in infants and young children"

1967   Prof R A Hinde "Experimental studies of mother/infant relations in monkeys"

1969   Dr J W B Douglas "Some happenings in childhood and their sequels"

1971   Prof H Harris "Genetic heterogeneity and the `inborn errors of metabolism'"

1973   Dr Elsie Widdowson "Cells, growth and function"

1975   Prof P E Polani "Sex determination and differentiation"

1977   Prof J L Emery "Unexpected death in infancy"

1979   Prof R H Haggerty "Life stress, social support and health"

1981   Dr Barbara Ansell "Chronic childhood arthritis today"

1983   Prof C B Blakemore "An experimental approach to the developmental disorders of vision"

1985   Dr J Tudor Hart "Wheezing in young children: problems of measurement and management"

1987   Prof Sir David Weatherall "The early prenatal diagnosis of genetic disease by fetal DNA analysis"

1989   Prof D Hull "Fever: the fire of life"

1991   Prof C H Rodeck "Fetal medicine – is it intrauterine paediatrics?"

1993   Prof Sir Michael Rutter "Attachment and social relationships: some implications for clinical practice"

1995   Prof E O R Reynolds, FRS "Understanding perinatal brain injury"

1997   Prof R E Petty "The legacy of George Frederic Still: finding order amid chaos"

1999   Prof N Hales "Programming during fetal life: consequences for adult disease and longevity"

Windermere Lecture
(Funded by Messrs Cow & Gate Nutricia Ltd)

The Windermere Lecture was named after the town in which the first and many subsequent Annual Meetings of the College were held.

RULES

1. That the lecture shall be known as the Windermere Lecture.

2. That it shall be given biennially by a paediatrician from abroad, to be selected by the Academic Board.

3. That the honorarium attaching to such lecture shall be £100.

4. That the expenses of the lecturer incurred at the Annual Meeting should be borne by the College.

LECTURERS

1948   Dr H Helmholz "Milk: a European child health problem"

1950   Prof A Wallgren "The declining birthrate. A medical and social problem"

1952   Prof R Debré "Miliary tuberculosis"

1954   Prof A Goldbloom "The evolution of the concepts of infant feeding"

1956   Prof L Emmett Holt, Jnr "Adolescence of nutrition"

1958   Prof Bo Vahlquist "Breast milk and cow's milk in infant feeding. A clinical, serological and biochemical study in 400 children"

1960   Prof J Lind "Aspects of the functional adaptation to extra-uterine life of newborn infants"

1962   Prof D B Jelliffe "Scientific paediatrics in developing regions: problems, perspective and progress"

1964   Prof A Prader "Studies on the effect of human growth hormone"

1966   Dr L Stanley James "The scientific basis for infant care in the perinatal period"

1968   Prof M Lamy "Immunologic deficiency disease in childhood"

1970   Prof C H Kempe "Paediatric implications of the battered child syndrome"

1972   Prof H Visser "Some physiological and clinical aspects of puberty"

1974   Dr D Pinkel "Acute leukaemia in childhood"

1976   Prof L Hanson "The rôle of E coli in infections of childhood"

1978   Prof M H Klaus "Parental attachment: a biological basis"

1980   Prof H Bickel "Inborn errors of metabolism – prevention and treatment"

1982   Prof Mary Ellen Avery "Our patients at highest risk: the new population of very low birth weight infants"

1984   Prof O Ransome-Kuti "The past, present and future of child health in Nigeria"

1986   Dr J Aicardi "Prenatal prevention of neurological disorders of childhood"

1988   Prof D M Danks "The present and future contributions of molecular genetics to the practice of paediatrics"

1990   Prof R Gorlin "35 years pursuing the Muse with only 15% success"

1992 Prof P D Phelan "Asthma – achievements and failures"
1994 Prof W A Silverman "The line between 'knowing' and 'doing': medicine's dilemma at the end of the twentieth century"
1996 Prof C Svanborg "Urinary tract infections in children: a model for studies on host parasite interaction"
1998 Prof P Gluckman "Treating perinatal asphyxia – the brave new world of neuronal rescue"

Winnicott Lecture
(Funded by The Winnicott Trust)

Donald Winnicott (1896-1971) was both a paediatrician and psychoanalyst. He was primarily interested in the effect of environmental factors on psychological development. Donald Winnicott was awarded the James Spence Medal by the British Paediatric Association in 1968. The Winnicott Trust supports research, including that into early mother-and-baby relationships at the Winnicott Research Unit at the University of Cambridge. To celebrate the centenary of Donald Winnicott's birth, the Winnicott Trust together with the Royal College of Paediatrics and Child Health inaugurated the Winnicott Lecture to be given at one of the College's meetings annually or biennially.

1997 Dr Lynne Murray "Developmental infant psychology"
1999 Dr Abraham Brafman " The child is still ill – how are the parents?"

Guthrie Medal

This award, made possible by a generous gift from the Action Research, was given in alternate years to an outstanding young medically qualified research worker in British paediatrics. The award consisted of a medal (known as the Guthrie Medal after Duncan Guthrie, former Director of the Fund) together with £300 to the medallist and a further £500 to the department in which he worked for the purchase of equipment or other expenses connected with his research.

Heads of Department were invited to submit names for consideration together with details of the research which may have been in any area of paediatrics. Nominees must have been below 36 years of age by 31 March in the year of the award.

The award was made on the recommendation of the Council of the British Paediatric Association after they had been advised by a special standing committee constituted for the purpose by the Academic Board.

The winner was invited to attend the Annual Meeting of the British Paediatric Association. Subsistence costs at the meeting were paid by the BPA and travelling expenses were paid from a legacy to the BPA by the late Dr Wilfrid Payne.

The award has been discontinued.

1976   Dr David Baum
1978   Dr David Davies
1980   Dr Michael Preece
1982   Dr Alan Lucas
1984   Dr Peter Fleming
1986   Dr Malcolm Levene
1988   Dr Andrew Pearson
1990   Dr Janet Eyre
1992   Dr Peter Clayton
1994   Dr Peter Scambler
1996   Dr William Reardon

Donald Paterson Prize

Donald Paterson (1890-1969) was a founder member and first Honorary Secretary of the British Paediatric Association. Latterly he returned to his native Canada to become Professor of Paediatrics in the University of British Colombia.

RULES

1. The competition will be called the Donald Paterson Prize.

2. The competition will be open to medical practitioners registered in the United Kingdom working in pre-consultant grades in the United Kingdom.

3. The competition will be held as often as the income from the bequest allows and if possible every two years.

4. The prize will be awarded to the author of the best article on any subject related to paediatrics which has been published within 2 years of the closing date in the advertisement, or which has been accepted for publication. The article will be judged with respect to scientific content, clinical contribution and presentation. The adjudicating panel may (in exceptional circumstances) award the prize jointly.

5. Advertisement of the prize competition will be made through the Newsletter of the Royal College of Paediatrics and Child Health, and if practicable in the British Medical Journal and the Archives of Disease in Childhood.

6. The advertisement will invite candidates to apply to the Royal College of Paediatrics and Child Health, including 3 reprints or pre-prints of the article they wish considered with their application. The application should also give details of name and address, medical school and date of qualification, and date of medical registration in the United Kingdom. If there is joint authorship the candidate will be required to submit an assessment of the contribution of the various authors, both to the study itself and to the writing of the paper. The adjudicating

panel may also invite suggestions from other sources; from editors of medical journals for example.

7. The articles submitted for the prize competition will be judged by an adjudicating panel constituted for the purpose by the Academic Board.

8. The winner will receive a monetary prize and will be invited to attend the Spring Meeting of the Royal College of Paediatrics and Child Health. Subsistence costs at the meeting will be paid by the College and travelling expenses will be paid from a legacy to the College by the late Dr Wilfrid Payne.

1964   Dr T D R Hockaday "The metabolic defect in primary hyperoxaluria" Arch Dis Child 1965; 40: 485-91

1966   Dr E M R Critchley "The social development of deaf children" J Lar Otol 1967; 81: 291-307

1968   Dr S R Meadow "The captive mother" Arch Dis Child 1969; 44: 362-67

1970   Dr M G H Rogers "Early recognition of handicapping conditions in childhood – theory and practice" Dev Med Child Neurol 1971; 13: 88

1972   Dr P M Jones "Growing up with haemophilia" Living with Haemophilia 1990; OUP, 3rd ed

1976   Dr J K Sarsfield "Rôle of house-dust mites in childhood asthma" Arch Dis Child 1974; 49: 711-15

1977   Dr J Graham-Pole "Granulocyte transfusion in treatment of infected neutropenic children" Arch Dis Child 1976; 51: 521-27

1979   Dr R J Levinsky "Circulating immune complexes in steroid-responsive nephrotic syndrome" N Engl J Med 1978; 298: 126-29

1981   Dr M I Levene "Cerebral structure and intraventricular haemorrhage in the neonate; a real-time ultrasound study" Arch Dis Child 1981; 56: 416-24

1983   Dr P Helms "Problems with plethysmographic estimation of lung volume in infants and young children" J Appl Physiol 1982; 53: 698-702

1985   Dr P T Rudd "A prospective study of chlamydial, mycoplasmal, and viral infections in a neonatal intensive care unit" Arch Dis Child 1984; 59: 120-25

1987   Dr C R Kennedy "The pathogenesis of virus-associated encephalopathies: a prospective study of immunological mechanisms" Clin Immun 1987; 42: 218-28

1989   Dr S J Newell "Gastro-oesophageal reflux in the preterm infant" Arch Dis Child 1989; 64: 780-86

1991   Dr K Pritchard-Jones "The candidate Wilms' tumour gene is involved in genito-urinary development" Nature 1990; 346: 194-97

1993 Dr D S Celermajer "Non-invasive detection of endothelial dysfunction in children and adults at risk of atherosclerosis" Lancet
1992; 340: 1111-15

1995 Dr W Reardon "Mutations in the fibroblast growth factor receptor
2 gene cause Crouzon syndrome" Nat Genet 1994; 8: 98-103

1997 Dr P J D Winyard " The PAX2 transcription factor is expressed in
cystic and hyperproliferative dysplastic epithelia in human kidney
malformations" J Clin Invest 1996; 2: 451-59

1999 Dr M Dattani "Mutations in the homeobox gene HESX1/*Hesx1*
associated with septo-optic dysplasia in human and mouse" Nat
Genetics 1998; **19**(2): 125–33

The Lorber Prize

John Lorber (1915-1996) was Professor of Paediatrics at the University
of Sheffield. He made major contributions to the field of medical ethics,
childhood tuberculosis and neural tube defects. The prize was established
in his memory by his wife.

RULES

1. The competition will be called the Lorber Prize.

2. The competition will be open to medical practitioners registered in the
United Kingdom, working in the United Kingdom in pre-consultant
grades at the time that the relevant scientific paper is accepted for
publication.

3. The competition will be held as often as the income from the bequest
allows and if possible every two years, alternating with the Donald
Paterson Prize.

4. The prize will be awarded to the author of the best article on any subject related to paediatrics which has been published within 1 year of the
closing date in the advertisement, or which has been accepted for publication. The article will be judged with respect to scientific content,
clinical contribution and presentation. The adjudicating panel may (in
exceptional circumstances) award the prize jointly.

5. Advertisement of the prize competition will be made through the
Newsletter of the Royal College of Paediatrics and Child Health, the
Association of Clinical Professors of Paediatrics, and if practicable in
the British Medical Journal and the Archives of Disease in Childhood.

6. The advertisement will invite candidates to apply to the Royal College
of Paediatrics and Child Health, including 3 reprints or pre-prints of
the article they wish considered with their application and a letter from
the editor, indicating the date that the paper was finally accepted for
publication. The application should also give details of name and
address, medical school, date of qualification and date of medical

registration in the United Kingdom. If there is joint authorship the candidate will be required to submit an assessment of the contribution of the various authors, both to the study itself and to the writing of the paper. The adjudicating panel may also invite suggestions from other sources; from editors of medical journals for example.

7. The articles submitted for the prize competition will be judged by an adjudicating committee established by the Academic Board of the Royal College of Paediatrics and Child Health and the prize will be awarded at the Spring Meeting.

8. The winner will receive a monetary prize and certificate which will be awarded at the Spring Meeting of the Royal College of Paediatrics and Child Health.

Dr Michael Blacow Memorial Fund

The Memorial Fund was established following a donation to the British Paediatric Association by Commander and Mrs A H Blacow in memory of their son, Michael, a trainee paediatrician who was killed in an accident. A money prize (currently £200) from the trust fund is awarded annually for the best paper presented in plenary session at the Annual Meeting by a paediatrician below consultant status. The prize cannot be awarded twice to the same trainee paediatrician. Selection of the prize-winning paper is made by the Academic Board.

1981   Dr J G Watson "Marrow transplantation in acute myeloid leukaemia"

1982   Dr M I Levene "The diagnosis and incidence of cerebral atrophy in the neonate by real-time ultrasound"

1983   Dr Janet Eyre "The diagnosis of seizures in the newborn by continuously recording the electroencephalogram"

1984   Dr M Levin "Pathogenic mechanisms in Kawasaki disease"

1985   Dr C R Kennedy "Aetiology, pathogenesis and prognosis in acute unexplained childhood encephalopathies"

1986   Dr K J S Anand "Should neonatologists be more concerned over the anaesthetic management of preterm neonates subjected to ligation of patent ductus arteriosus?"

1987   Dr Linda Lashford "The development of 'targeted' radiotherapy to treat central nervous system tumours"

1988   Dr T H H G Koh "Electromagnetic stimulation of the motor cortex; a simple and painless technique to measure objectively corticospinal tract function in newborn babies and children"

1989   Dr C M Evans "T cell-mediated changes in epithelial cell proliferation and goblet cell numbers in human fetal colon: a model of colitis"

1990   Dr Peta Sharples "Are children with head injury subjected to iatrogenic ischaemic injury?"

1991 Dr A G Stuart "Cerebral glucose production; evidence for disruption of astrocyte glycogen homeostasis in children undergoing major surgery"

1992 Dr C G Steward "The impact of clonal change on PCR assessment of minimal residual disease in ALL"

1993 Dr R J Forsyth "Evidence for significant glucose-6-phosphatase activity in astrocytes: a basis for local glucose homeostasis within mammalian brain"

1993 Dr Deborah Matthews "Evidence for progressive cerebral mitochondrial dysfunction in severely head-injured children"

1994 Dr W Tin "The changing prognosis for babies born more than eight weeks early over the decade"

1995 Dr P Heath "Invasive haemophilus influenzae infection following Hib immunisation"

1996 Dr K J Lindley "Nesidioblastosis – an enigma finally explained from studies of the KAPT channel"

1997 Dr J L Craze "Outcome for Down syndrome children with acute myeloid leukaemia in the United Kingdom, 1987-1995"
   Dr K Matyka "Nocturnal hypoglycaemia in prepubertal children with insulin dependent diabetes mellitus"

1998 Dr E G H Lyall "High uptake of interventions to prevent mother to child transmission of HIV by women aware of their HIV status"

1999 Dr C M Healy "Characteristics of infants of Hepatitis C infected mothers in the Republic of Ireland"

Babes in Arms Travelling Fellowships

The charity "Babes in Arms" offers Travelling Fellowships up to £3000 to paediatricians in higher professional training undertaking research into sudden infant death syndrome or associated problems.

Heinz Fellowships

1. Two or three fellowships will be offered each year, the number and type awarded in any one year depending on circumstances and the calibre of the applicants available.

2. The types of fellowships, which are open to men and women, are:

FELLOWSHIP A
To enable a paediatrician from any part of the Commonwealth overseas to spend up to twelve weeks in the United Kingdom meeting British paediatricians and seeing something of their work.

FELLOWSHIP C
To enable a paediatrician from the United Kingdom of Registrar, Senior Registrar, Specialist Registrar or Consultant status, or other member of the Royal College of Paediatrics and Child Health but in the early years of

professional life to make a short working visit (up to three months) to a centre in a developing country, teaching or conducting research so as to benefit both the Fellow and his hosts. The applicant should submit a brief programme and indicate the likely benefits to himself and to his hosts which he suggests will accrue.

3. Further details and application forms are obtainable from the Royal College of Paediatrics and Child Health.

Visiting Fellowships

The Visiting Fellowships were established in 1993 to enable young paediatricians from abroad to visit the United Kingdom. The Fellowships allow attachment to a paediatric department for three weeks and attendance at the College Spring Meeting. The Fellowships are funded by a levy on subscriptions paid by Ordinary and Associate Members of the College.

Two Fellowships which are normally for up to six weeks each, are in memory of Professor Donald Court, former President of the BPA and are specifically for a trainee or team member in community child health from Eastern Europe and former Soviet Union. These Fellowships allow attachment to a unit practising disability care or child protection and attendance at the College Spring Meeting. These Fellowships are supported by a fund established by the British Association for Community Child Health.

Children Nationwide Paediatric Research Fellowships

The Fellowships are awarded jointly by the Royal College of Paediatrics and Child Health and the Royal College of Physicians of London. These scholarships were established by a generous endowment of £250,000 by the Children Nationwide Medical Research Fund. The Fellowships are given for a two year period; one is open for competitive application each year and is usually awarded in the early months of the year. Applications are accepted from individuals or from paediatric units or research departments applying on behalf of individuals.

1986	Dr M Young	1989	Dr K J Lindley
1987	Dr J E Thomas	1990	Dr Fiona Campbell
1988	Dr F E M Jewkes	1993	Dr C W Yoxall

Douglas Hubble Travel Bursary

The Douglas Hubble Travel Bursary was established in memory of Sir Douglas Hubble, Emeritus Professor of Paediatrics and Child Health in the University of Birmingham who died in 1981. Sir Douglas Hubble was the first Chairman of the Academic Board of the British Paediatric Association (1966–69). The award is administered jointly by the University of Birmingham and the Royal College of Paediatrics and Child Health.

The award provides financial support for young paediatricians, or paediatric research workers below consultant rank, to present scientific papers at meetings within Europe but outside the UK, or to visit institutions overseas to learn techniques or acquire experience which would be a benefit to British paediatric practice. Applications enclosing a summary of the work to be presented and a supporting letter from a RCPCH member should be submitted to the RCPCH office by 1 March each year.

1986	Dr Linda Lashford	1989	Dr Kevin Forsyth
1987	Dr Simon Bignall	1991	Dr Heather Coughtrey
1987	Dr John Puntis	1993	Dr Keith Lindley
1987	Dr Martin Young	1995	Dr Leena Patel
1988	Dr Bhupinder Sandhu	1997	Dr Jonathan Hourihane
1988	Dr John Gibbs	1999	Dr Heather Elphick

Until further notice, this bursary will be awarded every two years.

Allen & Hanburys Research Award

These awards were established in 1990 to enable young United Kingdom paediatricians or research scientists (up to consultants of not more than five years' standing) to make short visits overseas to learn new research techniques, establish collaborative research or to acquire new clinical research skills. Each award is of up to £3000. Applications, consisting of a research programme, a letter of acceptance from the host institution, a letter of support from the applicants' head of department, and the applicants' curriculum vitae were submitted to the RCPCH office. Discontinued in 1999.

1990	Dr Ian Sanderson	1996	Dr Gareth Evans
1991	Dr Charles Buchanan	1996	Dr Brendan Harrington
1991	Dr Andrew Cant	1996	Dr Robert McClure
1991	Dr Joanne Clough	1996	Dr Christopher O'Brien
1992	Dr Jonathan Grigg	1996	Dr Paul O'Keefe
1992	Dr Gopikumar Menon	1996	Dr Andrew Pollard
1992	Dr David Thomas	1997	Dr Robert Forsyth
1993	Dr Alistair Baker	1997	Dr Jocelyn Glazier
1993	Dr Mark Everard	1997	Dr Paul Kemp
1993	Dr Melanie Newport	1997	Dr Shamima Rahman
1994	Dr Sailesh Kotecha	1997	Dr Anne Slavotinek
1994	Dr Deb Pal	1998	Dr Phillipa Clark
1995	Dr Stephen Cronin	1998	Dr Joyce Plested
1995	Dr Mark Hayden	1998	Dr June Nunn
1995	Dr Gideon Lack	1998	Dr John Achermann
1995	Dr Elizabeth Towner	1998	Dr Seamus O'Neill
1996	Dr Richard Brooker	1998	Dr Julie Williams
1996	Dr Suzanne Crowley		

SPARKS Young Investigator of the Year Medal

This award is generously funded by SPARKS (Sport Aiding Medical Research for Kids), is given annually for excellence in research to an outstanding young medically qualified research worker in British paediatrics. The award consists of a medal, together with £500 to the medallist, and a further £500 to the department in which they work for the purchase of equipment or towards other expenses connected with their research.

Heads of departments are invited to submit names for consideration, together with details of the research, which may be in any area of paediatrics, but must have been conducted while in a pre-consultant post. Nominations will be considered by an adjudicating panel constituted for the purpose by the Academic Board.

The winner will be invited to attend the Spring Meeting at which a presentation will take place; subsistence costs at the meeting and travel expenses will be paid by the College.

1999   Dr Jeremy Hull

Medical Student Prizes

A number of medical students are invited to attend the Spring Meeting as guests of the College. The students are selected on the basis of a recommendation from their head of department. It is hoped that the sponsorships will encourage students to pursue a career in paediatrics. The scheme has operated every year since 1991; twenty two students attended the Spring Meeting in 1999. The prize is funded by the College.

Bye-Laws of the College

1. Interpretation
    (i)   In the event of any inconsistency between the provisions of the Charter and the provisions of the Bye-Laws the provisions of the Charter shall prevail.
    (ii) In these Bye-Laws, unless the context otherwise requires, the expressions or words used in the Charter shall have the meanings there defined.
    (iii) In these Bye-Laws "the Charter" shall mean the Royal Charter incorporating the Royal College of Paediatrics and Child Health.
    (iv) In these Bye-Laws "the Regulations" shall refer to the Regulations of the College for the time being made under Article 12 of the Charter. Until the first General Meeting, the Regulations shall be those Bye-Laws and Standing Orders binding the British Paediatric Association as at the date of the Charter, save and insofar as the same are inconsistent with these Bye-Laws.

2. The Composition of the Council

The Council of the College shall consist of the Officers of the College and:-

(i)   (a) one representative elected by the Fellows and Ordinary Members of the College resident in each of the 14 regions of England as originally defined by and under section 8 of the National Health Service Act 1977;

     (b) one representative elected by the Fellows and Ordinary Members of the College resident in Wales;

     (c) three representatives elected by the Fellows and Ordinary Members of the College resident in Scotland;

     (d) one representative elected by the Fellows and Ordinary Members of the College resident in Northern Ireland;

     (e) one representative elected by the Fellows and Ordinary Members of the College resident in the Republic of Ireland;

     (f) two representatives elected by the Associate Members of the College resident in the United Kingdom and Ireland;

     (g) two representatives elected by Ordinary Members who are in training within the National Health Service;

     (h) a nominee of the Association of Clinical Professors of Paediatrics;

     (i) two representatives elected by conveners of specialty groups affiliated to the College.

(ii) Save for the nominee of the Association of Clinical Professors of Paediatrics:

     (a) the Members of the Council so elected shall serve initially for three years, whereupon they must retire or offer themselves for re-election;

     (b) if re-elected, Members of the Council may serve for a further two years, after which they must retire and may not offer themselves for re-election.

In each case, prior service as elected Members of the Council or Officers of the British Paediatric Association shall count as though it were service on the Council of the College and the first Members of the Council and Officers of the College shall be those who were serving the like office within the British Paediatric Association at the date of the Charter.

(iii) The procedure for the nomination and election of Members of the Council shall be defined by the Council in Regulations.

3. Officers

The Officers of the College shall be:-

(i)   the President;

(ii) the President Elect;

(iii) the Honorary Treasurer;

   (iv) the Honorary Secretary;
   (v)   the Honorary Editor;
   (vi) the Chairman of the Academic Board;
   (vii) two Vice Presidents;
   (viii)the Director of Research;
   (ix) not more than nine other Officers.

4. Mode of Election of Officers
    (i)   All candidates for election as Officers of the College must be nominated by at least two Ordinary Members or Fellows of the College.
    (ii)   The President shall be nominated by at least six Fellows or Ordinary Members. The President shall be elected by postal ballot of Ordinary Members and Fellows using the alternative vote system, save that the accidental omission to send nomination forms or ballot papers to any person entitled to receive these shall not invalidate the Presidential Election.
    (iii) Honorary Officers and the President shall be Fellows of the College and they should hold office for the following terms:
        (a)   The President shall serve for one year after election as President Elect and the following three years as President;
        (b)   The Honorary Secretary shall serve for one year as Honorary Secretary Elect and the following three years as Honorary Secretary;
        (c)   The Chairman of the Scottish Committee shall be elected by a postal ballot of Ordinary Members and Fellows who are resident in Scotland and will serve a fixed term of three years;
        (d)   Other Officers shall serve for a period of three years from their election.

        The term of all the Officers save for the President and the Chairman of the Scottish Committee may be extended by a further two years only by a decision of the Council. Upon the completion of their term of office Officers shall not be eligible to stand for re-election.
    (iv) Nominations for Officers other than the President being duly proposed and seconded by two Fellows of the College shall be submitted to the Honorary Secretary at least three months before the Annual General Meeting. The Vice Presidents, Honorary Secretary, Treasurer, and Chairman of the Academic Board shall be elected by a postal ballot of Ordinary Members and Fellows using the alternative vote system. Council shall consider nominations and elect the other Officers.
    (v)   The Council shall be empowered to co-opt any Members to serve on Standing Committees, Working Parties and to act as Representatives on outside bodies.

5. Members
    The members of the College shall be:-
    (i)   *Ordinary Members*, who may use the designation MRCPCH shall
          be those who, at the date of the Charter, are Ordinary Members
          of the British Paediatric Association and
          (a)   those medical practitioners who pass the examination for
                membership of the College in accordance with the
                Regulations;
          (b)   those medical practitioners who are otherwise granted the
                title Member of the College by the Council of the College by
                election in accordance with the Regulations;
          (c)   others who may be granted the title Member of the College
                by the Council in accordance with the Regulations but who
                shall consist of not more than 5% of the total College mem-
                bership at any time.
    (ii) *Fellows* of the College shall be selected by the Council from
          amongst the Members in such manner as may from time to time
          be prescribed by the Regulations of the College. They may use the
          designation FRCPCH.
    (iii) *Honorary Fellows* The College shall have the power to elect as
          Honorary Fellows such persons and in such manner as the
          Regulations of the College may provide and to permit Fellows so
          elected such privileges other than that of voting as members of the
          College as may from time to time be conferred upon them by or
          under the Bye-Laws. The Honorary Members as at the date of the
          Charter shall be elected Honorary Fellows. All Honorary Fellows
          may use the designation Hon. FRCPCH.
    (iv) *Associate Members* The Council shall have the power to appoint as
          Associate Members of the College those who at the date of the
          Charter were Associate Members of the British Paediatric
          Association and other medical practitioners who are elected as
          Associate Members by the Council in accordance with the
          Regulations of the College.
    (v)   *Overseas Members* shall be those who:
          (a)   were at the date of the Charter, Overseas Members of the
                British Paediatric Association;
          (b)   are elected Overseas Members by the Council after passing
                the examination for membership of the College in accor-
                dance with the Regulations.
                They shall have the right to vote at meetings which they
                attend in person but not to take part in postal ballots.
    (vi) *Senior Members and Fellows* shall be those Members and Fellows of
          the College or the British Paediatric Association who have
          attained the age of 65 years or who declare themselves to have
          retired permanently from clinical practice. They shall only be enti-
          tled to those voting rights conferred from time to time by the

Regulations and they shall be eligible to pay a reduced subscription as shall be laid down in accordance with the Regulations. They may use the designation MRCPCH or FRCPCH as they were entitled formerly.

(vii) *Junior Members* Those who have commenced training in the specialty of Paediatrics but who have not yet passed the examination for membership of the College in accordance with the Regulations may nevertheless be admitted to junior membership of the College by a decision of the Council. They shall be eligible to pay such subscription and shall have such rights as may be laid down from time to time in the Regulations.

6. Termination of Membership

Any members may be dismissed from membership of the College if:-

(i) found by the Professional Conduct Committee of the General Medical Council to have been convicted of a criminal offence;

(ii) judged by the Professional Conduct Committee of the General Medical Council to have been found guilty of serious professional misconduct;

(iii) judged by the Council to have behaved in a manner prejudicial to the welfare or good name of the College.

Provided that no member shall be dismissed from membership of the College, unless their name has first been erased from the Medical Register by the General Medical Council as a result of a Hearing before the Professional Conduct Committee, without being given the right to attend and be heard by the Council in accordance with the Regulations before the decision is made. The Regulations shall respect the rules of natural justice enabling the member to have sight of the case against him, the right to be represented and the right to call witnesses on his own behalf and the right to cross-examine witnesses called against him.

7. Fees and Subscriptions

(i) The subscriptions for the different categories of membership shall be such sums as shall be set by the Council and shall be due on the dates prescribed by the Council.

(ii) Any member who is more than 12 months in arrears and who has been notified in writing shall cease to be a member of the College unless a subscription is received within 60 days of the date of despatch of the written notification to the member's registered address unless the Honorary Treasurer has exercised his power under the Regulations to waive or lower the sum due.

(iii) Members removed under this rule may be reinstated by Council without undergoing the normal election procedure.

8. General Meeting
   (i) The Annual General Meeting of the College shall be held once in every year at such place and such time (being not less than two months after the date of such determination) as the Council may determine, provided that no more than 15 months shall elapse between such meetings.
   (ii) The President or the Council may at any time convene an Extraordinary General Meeting of the College and the Council shall convene such a meeting whenever so required in writing by not less than 5% of the Ordinary Members and Fellows of the College. At least 21 days notice of every General Meeting of the College (exclusive of the day on which the Notice is served but inclusive of the day for which the meeting is called) specifying the place, day and hour of the meeting and the general nature of the business to be transacted shall be given by notice sent by post to every member of the College.
   (iii) The accidental omission to give notice of a General Meeting of the College to any person entitled to receive such notice shall not invalidate anything done at such meeting.
   (iv) At all general meetings of the College the Officers and Ordinary Members and Fellows shall, if personally present, be entitled to one vote. No other person shall be entitled to vote.
   (v) A person otherwise entitled to vote who has not paid every subscription or other sum due and owing by him to the College shall not be entitled to vote.
   (vi) The business to be transacted at the Annual General Meeting of the College shall consist of:-
      (a) The presentation of the accounts and balance sheet of the College and of the Annual Report of the Council.
      (b) The appointment of the College's auditors.
      (c) Such other business as may be decided by the Council or submitted in writing to the Honorary Secretary not less than 10 weeks before the date of the meeting, accompanied by the signatures of 15 Ordinary Members or Fellows.

   One-fortieth of the Ordinary Members or Fellows entitled to vote being personally present shall constitute a quorum. If within half an hour from the time appointed for the holding of a General Meeting a quorum is not present the meeting shall be dissolved.
   (vii) The President shall be entitled to take the Chair at every General Meeting of the College. If the President is not present at the time appointed for such meeting the Chair shall be taken by the Senior of the Vice Presidents and in the absence of them both the members present shall choose one of their number to take the Chair.
   (viii) If within half an hour of the time appointed for the meeting a quorum is not present the meeting shall stand adjourned to such

day (not being more than twenty-one days thereafter) and at such hour and place as the Chairman thereof shall determine, and if at such meeting a quorum is not present those persons who are then and there present entitled to vote (being not less than 11) shall be a quorum and may transact the business for which the meeting was called.

(ix) Every question submitted to a General Meeting shall be decided by a show of hands of those entitled to vote and by a majority of such votes. In cases of doubt or whenever he deems it expedient, the Chairman of the Meeting may call for a secret ballot. In the case of an equality of votes the Chairman of the Meeting shall have a second or casting vote. Voting by proxy shall not be allowed.

(x) At any General Meeting a declaration by the Chairman of such a meeting that a resolution has been carried or carried by specific majority or lost or not carried by specific majority, and an entry to that effect in the Minute Books of the College, shall be conclusive evidence of the fact without proof of the number or proportion of the votes recorded in favour of or against such resolution.

(xi) The Chairman of the Meeting may with the consent of the majority of persons present and entitled to vote adjourn it from time to time and from place to place.

(xii) Regulations may provide for the further conduct of the meeting.

9. Auditors
    The Auditor or Auditors who shall be qualified in accordance with the Charter shall be elected annually at the Annual General Meeting. A retiring Auditor or Auditors shall be eligible for election. If the Auditor resigns in the course of the year a successor chosen by the Council shall be ratified at the next General Meeting.

10. Minutes
    The Honorary Secretary shall cause Minutes of all meetings of the College, the Council and the duly appointed Sub-Committees of the Council to be entered into a Minute Book.

11. The Council Powers
    (i) The management of the affairs of the College shall be vested in the Council, which in addition to the power and authorities expressly conferred on it by these Bye-Laws or otherwise, may in respect of the affairs of the College exercise all such powers and do all such things as may lead to the furtherance of the objects of the College, including all such powers and things as may be exercised or done by the College and are not by these Bye-Laws exercised or done by the College in General Meeting.

(ii) The Council shall consist of those who shall be elected or nominated as herein provided.

(iii) The Council shall have power from time to time to co-opt as an additional member of the Council any person who is an Ordinary Member or Fellow of the College. Any person so co-opted shall hold office until the next Annual General Meeting but may again be co-opted at any time.

(iv) The Council may act notwithstanding any vacancies in its numbers but if at any time the number of Members of the Council is reduced below twenty Members, the Council shall act only for the purpose of filling up vacancies among the Members or convening a General Meeting of the College.

(v) Any Officer or Member of Council shall vacate office and cease to be such a member if:-

    (a) he becomes incapable of exercising his function as such a Member;

    (b) if a Bankruptcy Order is made against him;

    (c) if by notice in writing to the Honorary Secretary he resigns from the Council;

    (d) if he ceases to be a member of the College;

    (e) if the College in General Meeting resolves that he shall retire.

12. Boards

The Council shall, at its first meeting after the Annual General Meeting in each year, elect Boards to deal with specific aspects of the work of the College for the purpose of making any enquiry supervising or performing any function or duty which in the opinion of the Council would be more conveniently undertaken or carried out by any such body. PROVIDED that all acts and proceedings of any such body shall be fully and promptly reported to the Council.

13. Quorum

The quorum for the Council shall be sixteen, one of whom shall be the President or Honorary Treasurer or the Honorary Secretary or one of the two Vice Presidents.

14. Voting

Motions at the Council, Executive Committee or the Boards of the College shall be passed by a simple majority and shall be countersigned by the Honorary Secretary or person appointed for the purpose by the Council. In the event of an equality of votes, the Chairman of the meeting shall have a second or casting vote.

15. The Executive Committee

The Executive Committee shall consist of the Officers of the College and up to three other Members of the Council. It shall have authority to deal with all matters as seem expedient and shall seek ratification of its decisions at the following meeting of the Council.

16. Seal

The Council shall provide for the safe custody of the common seal of the College which shall not be used except with the authority of the Council and in the presence of at least two Members of the Council who shall sign the instrument to which the seal is affixed and every such instrument shall be countersigned by the Honorary Secretary or person appointed for the purpose by the Council.

17. Investments

The Council shall have the power to employ as a professional investment manager any person who is entitled to carry out an investment business under the provisions of the Financial Services Act 1986 and to delegate to any such manager ("the Manager") the exercise of all or any of the powers of investments on such terms and at such reasonable remuneration as the Council may see fit but always subject to the following:-

(i) Delegated powers shall be exercisable only within the clear policy guidelines drawn up in advance by the Council and within the powers of investment allowed by law;

(ii) Every transaction carried out by the Manager under delegated powers shall be reported to the next meeting of the Executive Committee;

(iii) The Council shall be entitled at any time and without notice to review, revoke or alter the delegation or the terms thereof;

(iv) The Council will be bound to review the arrangements for delegation at least once in every 12 months.

18. Accounts

(i) The Council shall cause true accounts to be kept of the receipts of expenditure of the College and the matters in respect of which such receipts and expenditure take place and of the assets, credits and liabilities and the sales and purchases of goods of the College. Proper books of accounts shall not be deemed to be kept if there are not kept such books of accounts as are necessary to give a true and fair view of the College's affairs and to explain its transactions.

(ii) At the Annual General Meeting of the College every year the Council shall lay before the meeting an income and expenditure account and balance sheet for the periods since the last preceding account, together with reports prepared by the Council and by the auditor or auditors. Copies of the accounts, balance sheet and reports shall be sent to all persons entitled to receive notices of General Meetings twenty-one days before the meeting, in the manner in which such notices are directed to be served as stated below.

(iii) The books of account shall be kept open to the inspection of members of the College and the auditor or auditors at the head-quarters of the College or such other places the Council shall see fit, during normal business hours.

(iv) The Council shall comply with its obligations under the Charities Act 1993 (or any statutory re-enactment or modification of that Act) with regard to:-

    (a) keeping accounting records for the College;

    (b) the preparation of annual statements of account for the College;

    (c) the auditing or independent examination of the statements of accounts of the College; and

    (d) the transmission of the statements of account of the College to the Charity Commissioners.

19. Notices

(i) Any notice sent by post to a member of the College shall be deemed to have been served on the third day following that on which it is posted and in proving such service it shall be sufficient to prove that the envelope or wrapper containing the notice was properly addressed to him at his registered address and stamped and posted.

(ii) Every member of the College shall from time to time notify the Honorary Secretary of an address which shall be his registered address and unless and until he has so notified his registered address he shall not be entitled to receive any notice of meeting of the College.

20. Indemnity

In the execution of the trusts of the College no Member of the Council shall be liable for any loss to the property of the College arising by reason of any improper investment made in good faith (so long as he shall have sought professional advice before making such investment) or for the negligence or fraud by any agent employed by him or by any other Member of the Council hereof in good faith (provided reasonable supervision shall have been exercised) by reason of any mistake or omission made in good faith by any Member of the Council hereof or by reason of any other matter or thing other than wilful and individual fraud, wrongdoing or wrongful omission on the part of the Member who is sought to be made liable.

Index